ELIZA LYNCH
REGENT OF PARAGUAY

by

HENRY LYON YOUNG

ANTHONY BLOND

First published in Great Britain 1966 by Anthony Blond Ltd., 56 Doughty Street, London W.C.1. © Copyright 1966 by Henry Lyon Young.

66 – 68117

Printed in Great Britain by W. & G. Baird Ltd., Belfast and bound by the Dorstel Press Ltd., Harlow.

CONTENTS

For Dorothy

CHAPTER ONE

PARAGUAYAN PROLOGUE

PARAGUAY was discovered by Sebastian Cabot in 1530 and claimed in the name of his patron the King of Spain. The Aborigines were Guarani. The word implies a warrior race but in reality the inhabitants were a docile people, trusting and easily subjugated. Under the laws of the Indies, the "Mitayos", otherwise the Indians, were declared freemen but a sort of serfdom prevailed whereby they were bound to serve their Overlords so many days a year. This system went by the name of "Yanaconas".

The first appointed Governor of the new Spanish Colony was the great Alvar Nunez Cabeza de Vaca. He was ship-wrecked off the coast of Florida, Argentina, and found wandering naked by the unhirsute Indians who took him to be a God because of his two beards one on his face and the other above his loins. Nunez adopted a policy of tolerance towards the Indian which earned him the disapproval and resentment of his countrymen. The Conquistadores were only interested in exploiting the natives and referred to them as "gente sin razon", unreasoning beings. The attitude of the Governor and his colonizers towards the conquered were at such variance that the Pope found it necessary to issue a papal bull on the 2nd June, 1537, declaring that the Indians of the New World were in reality men (as opposed to animals) and therefore eligible to embrace the faith of Christ.

The Indians proved easy to convert and were baptized by the thousands though how they could have understood the Holy Mysteries without speaking the language of the priests seems to have puzzled Cunningham Graham but, as he says, "The word of God passeth all understanding."

1

Those converted to Christianity lived in Pastoral Communities established by the Jesuits known as "Missiones"; to the villages they gave the name of "Capillas" or chapels. The territory was fertile and crops were raised with the minimum of labour. It has been said that six hundred thousand head of cattle were husbanded by one hundred thousand men. From the first the Jesuits treated the Indians like grown up children. Hardly a day passed that they did not celebrate some Saint's day or hold a religious festival. Life was a perpetual Sunday. The rhythmic routine of sermons, prayers, liturgies and offices of the day found a ready response in the native mind and filled the Indians with religious ecstasy. Music came to them naturally and they sang Gregorian chants in Guarani. Francois-Xavier de Charlevoix of the company of Jesus wrote in 1756 that "they learnt as if by magic to play on any instrument." The communities built their own churches as ornate and Baroque as any to be found in Germany or Spain. They carved pulpits, sculptured Saints and mastered the art of polychrome. Vestments were embroidered and intricate altar cloths were woven. Nor was this all: church organs were made by hand, gilded and lacquered, and even astronomical instruments were chiselled by the Guarani. There was not an object that they could not copy, yet they were unable to express one original thought or create an object of their own initiative.

For nearly two hundred years the Guarani lived in this dream-like state, cloistered and secluded, but hardly monastic, for the Society of Jesus encouraged matrimony as an honourable state that more children might be procreated to sing the praises of the Lord. The only clouds on the horizon were occasional skirmishes with the "Banderistas", Brazilian buccaneers who swept down from the province of Sao Paolo and invaded the peaceful missions. Father Ruiz Montoya, in his "Spiritual Conquest of Paraguay" describes an occurrence when, at the head of a group of Indians, he resisted an attack from the Paulistas and made the scathing remark, "The monkey is not a Christian".

Then came a thunderbolt. The Jesuits were expelled from Paraquay. In the mother country it was maintained that the Society of Jesus was usurping the authority of the Crown. Exaggerated rumours of wealth and stories of supernatural powers were attributed to them and His Majesty was prevailed upon to recall the order in 1767. The defence of the Indian from the exploitation of the Spaniard had been their downfall. Had the Jesuits been guilty of the crimes ascribed to them, they could have put five thousand members of their order in the field as well as countless Indians and overcome the scanty Spanish garrison. Instead, they departed in silence, deeply hurt but grateful to God for His lesson in humility. Without the protection of their benefactors the Guarani reverted to a primitive state, and became listless, childlike and helpless.

Soon the Baroque churches were cobwebbed and colonies of bats flew blindly through the deserted missions. The once ploughed fields were neglected and macaws, uttering their harsh cries, fluttered across the open spaces. Monkeys chattered in the trees, wild horses snorted and took fright and the encroaching forest overran the chapels, as if the jungle once again reclaimed her own. When, on rare occasions, a Franciscan, long the enemy of the Jesuit, visited the neglected flock, the people came from miles around to hear him preach. Endless processions of Indians walked through the night making strange flapping noises with their feet. Spectral as the dawn, they seemed to be as one with the forests which they traversed. The men wore white shirts and drawers fringed with lace while the women were attired in white chemises edged with black, called "Tupois". Their hair was cut square over the forehead and hung loosely down the back like the coarse black mane of a wild mare. Once they reached some neglected chapel in the woods, they squatted on the ground and waited patiently, sometimes for hours, for their shepherd to begin the half forgotten ritual.

In this outpost, situated nearly a thousand miles from Buenos Aires time seemed to be arrested. The old patrician families, jealously guarding their pure white blood, were interrelated by a series of consanguineous marriages. They lived in semi-feudal style on large estates, administered in a fatherly way; and if they had no great herds of cattle like the Hacendados in the Argentine, they had time as they said to listen to their lives.

The great wealth of these descendants of Spaniards lay in their silver plate, mate pots and platters, washbasins and jugs, eating utensils and pots-de-chambre and silver trappings for their horse.

One story adobe houses, colonnaded and red-tiled, built around an inner patio concealed many a contented slave who slept all day, barely arousing himself to pick an orange off a tree; while the lady of the house reclined on a hammock, swinging herself gently to and fro with her big toe, a digit that developed out of all proportion, and hindering her from wearing, with any comfort, high heeled slippers at the dances in Asuncion.

CHAPTER TWO

END OF THE COLONY

At the beginning of the nineteenth century, Parish Robertson, a young Scotsman, attended a fiesta held in honour of Saint John of Itapua at the house of dona Juana Ysquibel, a distinguished matriarch. All classes were represented from the members of the Government to the shopkeepers of Asuncion. Preparations were set in motion weeks beforehand. An image of John the Evangelist, dona Juana's most treasured possession was taken out of its glass case in the drawing room and given a polish. All the worthy matrons of Asuncion outvied each other in presenting him with a garment worthy of the occasion. One devout lady sat up all night making the Saint a black velvet robe. Another trimmed the garment with yards of gold lace. Yet a third lent him her best opals and the most God fearing beata of all went so far as to sew her pearls on to his sandals.

On the actual day of the feast the image was set in a grotto of artificial rocks, seashells and moss which stood at the end of the garden. Towards evening, barefooted girls lighted the candles and illumined the shrine. Then, from afar, was heard the jingle of the silver rowels which announced the advancing cavalcade. A band of musicians on horseback composed of members of the Franciscan order headed the procession. The friars encountered the utmost difficulty in restraining their steeds from trotting while trying to read the sheets of parchment set before them on music stands attached to the pummel of their saddles. The sound of martial music rent the air played disjointedly and spasmodically on flutes, mandolines and trombones.

After the Franciscans came the Dominicans, who in turn

were followed by the monks of the Recoleta riding on richly
caparisoned donkeys. In a stream of dust and good humour
the guests approached in every kind of conveyance. Young
men wearing ponchos draped swaggeringly over the
shoulder rode on horseback seated on high-backed native
saddles encrusted with silver nuggets. Oxen carts covered in
awning creaked along the uneven roads conveying many a
mother and her daughter reclining on cushions on the floor.
One of the wagons contained don Gregorio de la Cerda, a
viejo verde, a dirty old man. He was the centre of a group
of adoring ladies whom he could not help pawing. Every
caress was received with squeals of delight or indignation.
In his wake came Doctor Burgos carried by slaves in a Sedan
chair. He was a mincing figure, powdered and corseted and
pomatumed. Immediately behind him drove the wives of the
four married members of the Junta in a state carriage well
over a hundred years old. Their husbands, who now held
the destiny of Paraguay in their hands, rode by their side on
high stepping horses trained in the Spanish school, each one
reminiscent of the Conde Duque de Olivares. Alone Doctor
Francia, the fifth member of the Junta, a spectral figure like
the ghost of Charles I, was missing and seemed the more conspicuous by his absence.

Finally came the late Spanish Governor in knee breeches,
silk stockings and a heavy sabre dangling from his saddle.
Although he had been deprived of his high rank he had
continued to live, highly honoured and respected, in the
country he had grown to love.

On their arrival at the Quinta, even before greeting their
hostess, the guests paid their respects to Saint John. They
knelt at his feet, crossed themselves and kissed his dress. To
all, peasant, horsemen and townspeople, invited and
uninvited, dona Juana extended a welcome. As each guest
entered the house she intoned the age old words "Ave Maria"
which were answered by the responsive ritual "Sin Pecado".
The humbler people formed into groups and played
"Tristes" melancholy tonadas on their guitars. But soon, with

the help of stimulating liquor, the sad melodies gave place to more spirited numbers. Fires were lit in the orchards casting their flickering light on the Grotto of Saint John before whom the revellers danced. Pungent, aromatic scents stirred the senses and perfumed the earth. Mothers invoked the Saint to protect their daughters. Fathers remembered that they were still men and sons planned many a campaign in which marriage was only a last resource.

As the hour advanced and the tropical moon hung suspended in the western hemisphere, the dancing became more lively. There was food and drink in abundance. Baby lambs and sucking pigs were roasted over sizzling spits in one orchard. Crystallized sweets and cakes of manjar blanco, the secret recipes of Spanish convents made their appearance on dona Juana's table, and when the dancing was at its height, the lady of the house was persuaded to take the floor. At the age of eighty-four dona Juana could still surpass her own grand-children in the intricacies of the steps and she still performed a lively Sarandig with Bedoya, a giant seven foot tall. Even the holy fathers were induced to join in the frolic and they lifted their cassocks and danced a jig. It was a patriarchial scene and the last great fiesta for decades to be held in Paraguay; even then the dread figure of Doctor Francia was lurking in the shadows, casting apprehension in the hearts of the dancers whose silhouettes were distorted in the dawn.

The last Spanish Governor seemed to have a presentiment for he turned round to the young Scotsman and said, "Ah, Mr. Robertson, I am afraid this is the last scene of festivity I shall ever see in Paraguay."

CHAPTER THREE

DOCTOR FRANCIA

PARAGUAY obtained her unwanted freedom on May 14th, 1811. The Republican ideas had come by way of Buenos Aires. For some time past the South American States had been agitating for their Independence. Loyalty to the King alone prevented them from realizing their ambitions. With the abdication of Carlos IV, however in favour of King Joseph Napoleon's brother, the colonies felt under no obligation to serve their new master and one by one broke the umbilical cord; by the time that Fernando VII, the rightful King, had reclaimed his father's throne it was too late to put back the clock. Paraguay, the most remote of all the South American States, cut off, as she was, by Brazil, Bolivia, Uruguay and the Argentine, alone resented this step and bitterly opposed General Belgrano who marched to Asuncion, at the head of a small army, to invite the Paraguayans to join the Argentine Confederation. He was met with fanatic resistance by a group of Militia headed by the effigy of Our Lady of Asuncion who was escorted to battle seated on a white horse.

Notwithstanding the passions aroused, Senor don Bernardo de Velasco, the Governor, a truly enlightened man realized the trend towards self-Government, and although he rejected the proposal of joining the Confederation, he bowed before the inevitable and signed the Declaration of Independence.

The last representative of the Crown retired into private life and the reins of Government were taken over by a Junta composed of five members among whom was Doctor Francia, a shadowy and sinister figure.

Don Jose Gaspar Rodriguez Francia was born in Asuncion on January 6th, 1758. He was of Portuguese extraction

8

through his father being a son of a don Garcia Rodriguez de
Francia, a Captain of Artillery in the Brazilian army. His
mother, on the other hand, dona Josefa Velasco y Yegros,
came of a long established but impoverished family in
Paraguay. Although Doctor Francia has often been accused
of having a touch of the tarbursh it seems unlikely or he
would not have been admitted into the University of Cor-
dova where boys were obliged to produce their pedigrees
and prove that they came of pure white stock. There, under
Jesuit tuition, he learnt mathematics, algebra, astronomy and
sufficient French to enable him to read Diderot or Voltaire in
the original. His intention had been to study for the priest-
hood, being one of the few professions open to those of
Spanish descent, but soon it became apparent that he had no
vocation for the Church and he applied himself instead to the
study of law.

On receiving his degrees, he returned to the city of his
birth and set up a legal practice and soon earned the respect,
if not the love, of his fellow citizens. In a country where
lawyers and men of letters were scarce he was one of the few
persons eligible to succeed the Spanish Governor when the
latter abdicated in favour of the Independence and was elected one of the Junta of five. But once having tasted power he
became voracious for more and would not be satisfied until
he had made himself absolute.

An opportunity arose when an envoy arrived from Buenos
Aires to negotiate a commercial treaty with Paraguay. Doctor
Francia cunningly retired to the country and events followed
as he foresaw. The bewildered members, unable to reach an
agreement among themselves, recalled him. To all their entreaties he turned a deaf ear. Finally he allowed himself to
be persuaded to return to the capital and addressed his colleagues as follows:
"This Assembly should not lose time in debating whether
the coward of a father or his more cowardly son is King of
Spain. Both of them have abdicated twice and both of them
have shown themselves to be weak of spirit and disloyal of

heart. Whether one or the other is King of Spain is no longer our concern. Neither of them is now King of Paraguay. Our country is no longer the patrimony of Spain, nor a province of Buenos Aires. Paraguay is an Independent Republic. The only question which should be debated in this assembly and unanimously put to the vote is—Who is to defend our rights and maintain our liberty from Spain, from Lima, Buenos Aires and Brazil? Who is to increase our prosperity and ensure the wellbeing of all the inhabitants of Paraguay?"

Needless to say he was elected to lead the country. His one condition was to rule alone. The Junta acquiesced and from then on he was known as "El Supremo".

Immediately the new Dictator showed his true colours and instituted a reign of terror. His late colleagues found themselves imprisoned on trumped up charges and even the last Spanish Governor was condemned to death for daring to criticize the new Dictator. Francia closed the boundaries to the outside world and subjugated the people. No foreigner was given the right to trade with Paraguay. He was so afraid of treachery that he went so far as to keep a British ship in quarantine for a week until he had mastered sufficient English to read the bill of lading. Monasteries, convents were closed down overnight as were centres of learning including the Colegio Carolino which had been founded in 1783. The reason being that Doctor Francia considered education an unnecessary evil. Courts of law and justice was administered by himself. A police service was established and an intricate spy system was evolved. Nothing went on in the country without his knowledge even to the very thoughts of the dying. He ruled without a constitution and Guarani replaced Spanish as the official language; scared by poverty in his youth he had an inborn hatred of the upper classes and wished to level all stratas of society, white, mestizo, Indian and Negro. The greatest humiliation he would bestow on a patrician family was to declare them officially mulatto. This was tantamount to exterminating the clan for it was inconceivable that these stiff-necked Spaniards could consort with any other class but their own. He would have liked to abolish marriage altogether but here he found that faith was stronger than reason. He therefore made it a condition that marriage was subject to his consent and a heavy tax was imposed.

Carlyle, the historian, admired him and professed an understanding of his character, that was melancholy and morose. He was a man who lived without a friend in the world, suspicious of his own shadow. In his defence it could be said that his rule was the rule of fear because the Guarani could understand no other method. If they had ever possessed a will of their own it had been drained out of them by the Jesuits. They were irresponsible, indolent people, ripe for a despot whom they got in the person of Doctor Francia. Carlyle goes on to assert that the Dictator's reason for closing the country to the outside world was founded on his observations on the other recently emancipated countries such as Chile, Peru and Argentine where a state of anarchy prevailed. It was a drastic step only intended as a temporary measure during the period of readjustment. The historian is convinced that but for Doctor Francia's policy of isolation, Paraguay would have found herself swallowed up by the Argentine confederation or annexed to Brazil. Paraguay may have paid dearly for his attitude but she saved herself the birthpangs of her neighbours and maintained her Independence.

Francia, a Voltairean and Agnostic, held the church in ridicule and never missed an opportunity to humiliate religion which he regarded as superstitious nonsense, an attitude that did not endear him to the Spanish nobility, who smouldered in impotent resentment. Sacrilegiously he had an engraving made of his likeness which he had placed on every altar and ordered the coat of arms of Paraguay to be carved above the portals of all churches to make it quite clear to the population that the State came before God. His favourite saying was Pan Pan. Vino Vino. . . Bread is Bread and Wine is Wine. In other words Give unto Caesar etc. . . On the other hand he never actually discouraged religious worship. The worst offence that can be laid to his charge is that he abolished free thinking. On the three hundredth anniversary of the founding of Asuncion which fell on August 15th, 1836, a delegation waited on Doctor Francia to ask permission to hold a religious procession in which the effigy of Our Lady of Asuncion would be paraded through the town. This was the same lady that had repulsed the forces of General Belgrano and had originally been brought from Spain by don Juan de Salazar y Espinosa in 1536.

The Dictator consented to the celebration on condition that dona Francisca Machain who held the hereditary right of guarding the blessed statue in her home should give up the privilege and return the Virgin at the end of the festivities to the church of la Encarnacion which would henceforth be its permanent home. Dona Francisca risked the wrath of the Dictator by refusing to give up her birthright; whereupon the procession did not take place.

The Supremo's palace was a low one-story building resembling a barracks. There was little luxury. Bare boards creaked underfoot. Barred windows looked out on to the muddy banks of the Paraguay and white washed walls stood naked and unadorned except for the reflection of his own shadow hunched over his desk working far into the night by the light of a green shaded oil lamp.

His habits were austere. In spite of retiring late he was up at dawn. His first act on waking was to summon his barber to come and shave him and to comb his periwig. He attended his multiple duties until midday with the aid of his faithful servant and secretary Policarpo Patino, a gentle scholarly man, avid for learning, who either through fear or love of Francia was devoted to labour. No detail of administration escaped him. It yielded him some satisfaction, we hope, that in the year 1833 Paraguay produced the best harvest within living memory. There was more wheat, peanuts, potatoes and sugar cane than could possibly meet the people's needs and still he refused to export the surplus convinced that the country was not yet ready to trade with the outside world.

Liberty must be earned, was an expression that he was fond of using.

Taciturn and solitary, implacable and a strict disciplinarian he dismissed the Collector of Taxes of Caazape for not being able to account for two Reales. At midday he ate a modest stew with mandiaoca and "chipa" after which he retired to the patio, buzzing with flies but fragrant with honeysuckle and jasmine, and stretched himself out on his hammock to enjoy a siesta. He ordered whole sections of the town, which were fever ridden, to be torn down and built in their place wide streets along which ran canals for irrigation. On the hills above Asuncion he erected a hospital and every morning rode forth to inspect the work in progress. At the sight of the Dictator dressed in black like a Cavalier, seated on a black horse, holding in his hands black velvet reins, the awe-stricken population prostrated themselves on the ground or hid behind closed doors. Yet there was another side to his character that few people had the chance to observe. A little girl playing in the streets of Asuncion looked up and found herself staring into the eyes of El Supremo. She was about to run away but he stopped to give her an orange and then proceeded on his way in silence . . . Too young to recognise compassion she was haunted by the expression on his face and ever after called him "El Triste Senor".

Solitary and silent he would return home again at dusk to resume work and partake of a frugal meal consisting of a breast of chicken and a glass of wine. Before retiring he would do his rounds and make certain that the doors of the Palace were barred and locked; he entrusted the keys to no one but himself. The last thing that he did at night was to place a revolver under his pillow. One solitary sentinel stood guard outside the Palace sheltered from the tropical storms in a striped sentry box, but a hundred yards away, in the military barracks, five thousand men were ready to carry out his commands. As a measure against insurrection no man in the army held the rank above that of Captain.

At his court there were no chamberlains, nor gold sticks in waiting. He was looked after by a cook, a chambermaid, a porter and an indoor servant, all of them mulattoes. A negro boy in a turban and the dog "Sultan" completed the family circle. It might well be said that the dog was his only friend for he ordered that the negro boy should be cast in prison for daring to hit his beloved animal. But later, when the boy attempted to escape, he countermanded the order and had him shot instead.

The Doctor never married but kept an account book, carefully balanced, in which he annotated his sexual prowess with the same sangfroid as if he was taking a purge. He had a daughter by one of the native women who followed in the footsteps of her mother and grew up to be a lady of easy virtue. She waylaid her clients outside her father's Palace, Although he never recognised her legally the Dictator displayed a sardonic sense of humour by making prostitution a highly respectable profession and determined that the girls should wear a golden comb as an insignia of their calling. From then on they were known as "Peinetes de Oro".

It was said of Francia that nobody thought he was human until he proved it by his death. This was a momentous event that took place on Christmas day of 1844 during a tropical thunderstorm like a finale to a Grand Opera. His death released the population from a state of subjection that they had endured for thirty years.

Francia, in spite of all his views on religion, was given a Christian burial with all the pomp and trappings of death that the priests could muster. But the primitive people were too afraid of his shadow to show themselves in the streets and few attended the obsequies except for the clergy and professional mourners who wept into long neck bottles under compulsion. The Priest, Father Perez, who delivered the funeral oration had the following to say . . . "His Excellency, the Dictator whose death we now lament and for whom we weep was the Saviour of our Country and the guarantor of our national freedom. What was Paraguay before him? What was

Paraguay before our Dictator took charge of her destiny? It was but the skeleton of a Colossus who needed a superhuman hand to clothe him in flesh and blood and to breathe life into him. Who else but Doctor Francia could have undertaken this Herculean task? Did he not protect our peoples from the perils that beset them at the outset of their freedom when they were at their most vulnerable. Was he not justified in employing every means at his disposal to safely deliver the new born nation? International peace and the security of the Republic were his only concern. I fear not to profane this Holy Ground by saying that God himself would have approved of his methods for the God of Wrath struck down his enemies with fire. But how must greater would our Dictator have been had he followed the teachings of Jesus Christ to obtain the same result?"

On this ambiguous note he crossed himself quickly and genuflected several times, looking round as if expecting to be struck by lightning.

Prior to interment the body of the Supremo was laid out in State before the High Altar of the Cathedral de la Encarnacion but during the night the cadaver disappeared giving rise to the legend that the devil had claimed his own. The mortal remains were never found. It was strongly suspected that the old Spanish families had out of revenge combined to throw it in the river for the alligators to eat. Whatever the reason it remained a mystery and the Paraguyans never again mentioned his name for fear of invoking his spirit and ever after referred to him in whispers as "El Difunto". "The Defunct One."

CHAPTER FOUR

SECOND DICTATOR OF PARAGUAY

FOR the second time in its short history Paraguay was ruled by a body of five men. The Junta formed a constitution and convoked a General Congress numbering three hundred members. From every province, from Itapua on the Parana, from Villa Rica, from the decaying Jesuit missions, a representative was elected and sent to the capital, the only qualification necessary was to read and write. But long before they reached Asuncion there was dissension among the members of the Junta and, in obeyance of the natural laws of the jungle, don Carlos Antonio Lopez had made himself absolute. This event took place on the 14th March, 1844. The new President lost no time in writing to the representative of the Argentine confederation and informing him of the fait accompli.

Asuncion; March 28th, 1844.

"Senor de Palermo,

The President of the Republic of Paraguay has the satisfaction of addressing himself to his Excellency the Governor of the Province of Buenos Aires, discharging the duties of Minister of Foreign Affairs of the Argentine Confederation and hereby gives him notice that according to the fundamental statute of the Republic of Paraguay sanctioned in General Congress by the most honourable members assembled, he has been designated President of the said Nation and has assumed the Supreme Authority as from 14th of the month in transit

Carlos Antonio Lopez
(Countersigned) Benito Martinez Varela."

Don Carlos Antonio Lopez, the second Dictator of Paraguay was born at La Recoleta, a village three miles out of Asuncion in 1787. He came of middle class parentage, that is a mixture of Spanish, Mulatto and Guarani. The father, a tailor by the name of Cirili Lopez, hoping to raise his son above his own station in life put him to study law and, in time, he fulfilled his parent's ambition. He obtained degrees in Latin, philosophy and theology and became a wellknown lawyer in Asuncion. Being of a shrewd disposition, however, he strove to appear as inconspicuous as possible during the reign of Francia who was jealous of all initiative but his own. When Carlos Antonio Lopez surprisingly married the stepdaughter of don Lazaro Rojas, a rich cattle owner, and member of an old patrician family, he gave up his legal practice in Asuncion and retired to the country to administer his wife's estates. Rumour, ever ripe in Asuncion, declared that Juana Pabla had got herself into trouble and that young Lopez had been bribed to make an honest woman of her. Whether there was any foundation or not in the slander he employed her fortune so advantageously that in a few years he had made himself President of the Republic.

There were five children of this marriage. Francisco Solano, born shortly after the marriage on the 24th July, 1826 or 1827, followed by Benigno, Venancio and two daughters, Innocencia and Rafaela. Envied and covertly ridiculed by the Spanish aristocracy the Lopez clan assumed the role of a parvenue Royal family, and took full advantage of their privileged position to increase their wealth. The Senora Presidenta proved that she had an acute business sense by commandeering all the cattle that came into the market at a fixed rate and reselling the herds at a profit. The daughters of the President had the monopoly of used bank notes. They bought them at a discount and changed them at the Treasury for their full value. Lopez, like Napoleon, had a strong family feeling and he placed his relatives in high positions to ensure his absolute rule. Even the church came under his domination when he persuaded Pope Gregory XVI to issue a papal bull naming his brother Basilio to the see of Paraguay, thus securing for his family the keys of Heaven and the riches of the Church.

Lopez was forty seven at the time of his predecessor's death. His portrait in Washburn's History of Paraguay depicts him as a gross looking man, a latin Falstaff, gluttonous and repellent. He was to be seen driving round the streets of Asuncion guzzling little cakes and throwing banana skins out of the carriage window. Never going to the extremes of Francia, he ordered the male population to buy hats that they might doff them in his presence. One of the first acts of the new President was to open up the country to the outside world and encourage trade. Foreigners were given the same privileges as those accorded to the citizens of Paraguay. Docks and arsenals were constructed. Nor was this all, with the help of an English engineer, Mr. Paddison, he built the first railway in Paraguay that ran from Asuncion to Paraguari, a distance of 72 kilometres. Don Carlos tried to promote friendly relations with his next door neighbours Argentine and Bolivia and it was due to his endeavours that England, France and subsequently the United States of America recognized the one time colony as an independent state and sent ministers to Asuncion, the seat of Government. During the twenty five years of his rule there was genuine prosperity in Paraguay; and on 24th November, 1842, the President took the unprecedented step of freeing the slaves and declared—"All men are equal before God and me."

This move was twenty years in advance of the United States and four years ahead of France, Sweden and Denmark.

The first newspaper to be published in Asuncion 'El Paraguayo Independiente" made its appearance in 1845. It was subsidized by the President and used as a medium for his literary talents. Every week he chose some enlightening homily for the good of his people. In his first year as President he opened four hundred and thirty two schools and enrolled 24,000 pupils. But all schools had to follow a certain curriculum set by himself. To encourage education he offered scholarships to universities abroad in chemistry, pharmacy,

law and medicine. It was fourteen years however, before anyone could avail themselves of this opportunity as a new genera-
tion had to grow up that knew how to read and write.

Lopez was a benevolent Dictator as long as everything proceeded to his liking but was quick to act if he thought he was
not receiving the proper attention. One day a merchant of
Asuncion presented himself at the Customs House to clear
some merchandise but was told that the value of the Government stamped paper needed to claim the articles was more
than he carried on his person. He lost his temper, tore the
document in shreds, trampled the pieces underfoot and left
the cargo unclaimed. In due course the incident was reported
to the President who immediately ordered the man to be shot
for daring to stamp on his effigy.

On another occasion the President came to loggerheads
with the United States over the Rhode Island Company, an
enterprise formed by a young man by the name of Hopkins
who had been appointed Acting American Consul and had
secured, without Lopez's knowledge or consent, the monopoly
of the yerba trade, Paraguay's main export, for five years, and
which Lopez felt was against the interests of Paraguay. Instigated by the President for his own motives, a row took place
between an American and a Paraguayan in which the latter
punched the former on the nose. Unfortunately the American
in question turned out to be Hopkin's younger brother. The
Acting American Consul stormed into the Dictator's presence
hatted, booted and spurred, contrary to all etiquette, and
demanded indemnities. Lopez protested indignantly but
ended the interview on a conciliatory note by ordering the
culprit to receive three hundred lashes. This sanguine method
of appeasement failed to satisfy Hopkins who felt he was entitled to monetary compensations and he appealed direct to
President Buchanan of the United States. The Republic of
the North sent a gun boat to press Hopkin's claims. Lopez had
no alternative, he settled the demands but made it a condition
that he kept the yerba trade for himself, a proposal that the

Americans conceded and which had been Lopez's objective all along.

Ever after the President boasted that he had won a great diplomatic victory over the United States. He released his spleen, however on the members of the community who had sold the concession to the American company and the Dictator arrested several worthy citizens on the trumped up charge of a conspiracy to overthrow him. It was unfortunate that among those imprisoned was a man by the name of Santiago Canstatt, a type only to be found in South America in those days. He was the Captain of a paddle steamer that sailed up and down the river Paraguay reminiscent of the show boats of the Mississippi. He was always impeccably dressed in a white drill suit with blue stripes and jipi papa hat. Don Santiago was known, as they say in Spanish, to owe a life or two, but that only enhanced his reputation. Lopez, unaware that Canstatt could claim British nationality (having been born of British parents in the Argentine) ordered his immediate detention. He was taken off his ship in fetters, plunged into prison and condemned to death. In reality he had only acted as agent in the transactions between Hopkins and the merchants of Asuncion. He appealed to the British Minister in Buenos Aires and the latter demanded his immediate release. Lopez was placed in a dilemma because he could not comply with the request without losing face nor did it suit him to be on bad terms with the British Government. He compromised by commuting the death sentence to one of life imprisonment hoping that the prisoner would expire of natural causes, an event that no doubt would have taken place had not the Hon. Edward Thornton, British Minister in Buenos Aires, retaliated in the most unexpected way. He took as hostage the President's son Francisco Solano Lopez.

CHAPTER FIVE

SPECIAL REPRESENTATIVE

FRANCISCO SOLANO LOPEZ was brought up to think of himself as a hereditary Crown Prince. Freely indulged from birth, he was arrogant and boastful. In spite of his doubtful parentage he was the apple of his father's eye and it was don Carlos who taught him his first letters. On the death of Francia his education was entrusted to a Jesuit priest by the name of Father Marco Antonio Maiz. The tutor was an aesthetic looking man barely ten years older than his pupil who tried to influence his charge for good but without much success. Francisco Solano had an exaggerated idea of his own importance. His favourite text book was "El Catecismo de San Alberto", a tome written in 1784 by the Bishop of Tucman, describing in detail how the insurrection of the Tupuc Amuru, the last descendant of the Incas, was put down with terrible severity by the Spaniards. It was meant (according to don Jose Estrada) to serve as a lesson in leadership, a lesson that Francisco Solano took very much to heart. Francisco's idol was Napoleon for whom he had a hero worship. There was no incident, however trivial, in the great man's life that did not interest him and he dreamed of moulding himself on the Emperor one day.

At the age of adolescence he was sexually precocious and displayed more than a healthy appetite for girls. He was a frequent habitué at the local brothel and when presented with the bill he exclaimed arrogantly "Send it to the Palace. Father will pay." Francisco was convinced that he had the droit de jambage and was entitled to any girl that took his fancy. But not all girls were his willing slaves and one in particular, Pancha Garmendia, rejected his advances. He persecuted her until she was forced to take refuge in a convent, a doubtful sanctuary because Lopez was known to have a penchant for nuns and some of the virgins indeed not averse to being Christian martyrs. To get him out of mischief don Carlos made his eldest son a Lieutenant Colonel and sent him on a campaign to Corrientes to win his spurs.

In 1846 Paraguay and the Argentine province of Corrientes signed an agreement whereby in case of aggression they undertook to give each other mutual aid. It was tacitly understood that any warlike action would be directed against them by the ageing Dictator Rozas who for thirty years had held the fate of Buenos Aires in his iron fist and not by the rest of the Argentine confederation. Lopez was well aware that Rozas resented the Independence of Paraguay and coveted the country. In reciprocation Corrientes promised to uphold the claim of Paraguay to the territory that lay beyond Tranqueno de Loreto and Aguapey on the borders of Brazil having as its limits the river Parana. But instead of being attacked by Buenos Aires Corrientes was besieged by General Urquiza, a man who was virtual Dictator of the Province of Entre Rios. Don Jose Justo de Urquiza, an aristocratic Gaucho, was a man of mystery. As powerful as a minor king, he refused to knuckle under to the Central power and was always playing one side against the other.

At this moment the spirit moved him to invade Corrientes which put the latter in a panic and Corrientes appealed to Paraguay for help. Although it was more than he bargained for don Carlos Antonio Lopez decided to stretch a point and send his eldest son to quell the revolution.

There were hysterical scenes in Asuncion as the young Lieutenant Colonel, who was barely nineteen, passed the troops in review. He presented them with new colours, red, white and blue in horizontal stripes. As Lopez stood before the recently designed Paraguayan flag he pressed it to his lips and with patriotic fervour said "I swear never to let go of this sacred emblem," words that were to become prophetic.

Francisco Solano left Asuncion at the head of his troops and marched to Villa del Pilar a provincial town tucked away in the interior of Corrientes to join forces with General Jose Maria Paz, commander-in-chief of the so called Pacifist army. By the time that Francisco Solano arrived the war was virtually over. No sooner had General Urquiza invaded Corrientes than the province capitulated without firing a shot and the belligerents signed a new pact called the Treaty of Alcaraz in which they formed an alliance promising each other mutual aid in case of aggression from the Central Government. All sides went home merrily as if nothing had happened and the campaign fizzled out. But Francisco Solano had not been idle. At Villa Rica he had a love affair with a girl called Juanita Pesoa, a typical Paraguayan beauty with sleek black hair, kiss curls licked into place and a high backed Spanish comb. He had one child by her and, when expecting another, he decided it was time to go home.

On his return to Asuncion Francisco fell passionately in love with Carmencita Cordal, a girl of good family who was about to marry her cousin Carlos Decoud. Francisco was resolved to make her his mistress and she was equally determined to resist him. Finally, on the eve of the nuptials, in a fit of jealous rage, Francisco had the bridegroom murdered and the body was thrown naked outside Carmencita's window to greet her on her wedding morning. She became insane and ever after was to be seen at the dead of night strewing flowers on her lover's grave like some strange exotic Ophelia.

The scandal had such far reaching repercussions that many long established families in Paraguay asked for their passports and left the country. The President raised no objection to their going as long as he could help himself to their property. At the same time he thought it would be wiser for Francisco to absent himself for a while and sent him on a mission to the Argentine to settle a dispute in the neighbouring Republic.

The Argentine Confederation was in a chronic state of civil war. General Urquiza, the perpetual trouble maker, had managed to overthrow the Rozas regime and had assumed the Presidency of the Confederation. The tyrant, meanwhile, had escaped the country in disguise on H.M.S. Locust and had settled down to farm quietly in Southampton. But don Justo Urquiza was hampered in his task of administration by the recalcitrance of Buenos Aires. This province had refused to ratify the treaty of San Nicolas which had unified the fourteen states and rose in revolt forcing Urquiza to withdraw to the provinces. For a period of years Buenos Aires had acted independently from the rest of the country and formed no part of the confederation, giving rise to the absurd situation that Urquiza was President of the entire nation except the capital, a state of affairs that could not go on indefinitely and he determined to bring matters to a head. The General marched on Buenos Aires at the head of an army of fifteen thousand men. In vain did the Hon. Benjamin C. Yancey, United States representative in Buenos Aires, try to intervene and to work out a peaceful solution but the placid American of the North could make little headway with the highly excitable Americans of the South. It was at this juncture that don Carlos Antonio Lopez, President of a friendly neighbouring Republic offered his services as mediator; a proposal that was immediately accepted by both sides and he entrusted the mission to his son. Thus far from falling into disgrace Francisco departed with full plenary powers and the newly acquired rank of General. He sailed for Parana, the seat of the Confederate Government with a highly colourful retinue that included two majors, four captains and eight lieutenants. By the time that he arrived at his destination, however, he was informed that an engagement had taken place at Cepeda between the troops of General Urquiza and the forces of General Mitre in which the latter had been completely routed and according to the latest reports, Urquiza had marched on the capital and was camping at the gates of Buenos Aires. The "Portenos", the citizens of Buenos Aires decided to resist him and built trenches, stored food and barricaded the streets.

Francisco Solano, as the peacemaker, summoned the leaders of the two contending parties and requested a ten day armistice. This initial move was followed by a conference held under his Chairmanship at the Chacra de Monte Caceros near Buenos Aires to which both sides sent representatives.

The young Paraguayan General opened the conference with the following words, "We meet here determined to conciliate all differences between the parties concerned and to help weld the confraternity of the Argentine." Ten days later, he ended the conference by saying "In spite of finding the Argentines under arms and stained with the blood of their brethren my estimation of their character has never wavered. All along I have been confident of reaching a peaceful solution and my highest hopes have been realized."

By his eloquence and rhetoric, Solano Lopez shamed the Argentines into accepting the fourteen points under discussion. Both sides consented to lay down their arms. Buenos Aires was reincorporated into the Argentine confederation and swore to uphold the Constitution. Urquiza consented to resign his seat of office and retire as Governor to his own province of Entre Rios holding in perpetuum the title "Founder of the National Unity of the Argentine Confederation." Mitre became Governor of Buenos Aires and new elections were held in which don Santiago Derqui, an innocuous individual, inoffensive to both sides, was elected President; and a vote of thanks was passed for Solano Lopez, who was the hero of the hour. It was a personal triumph. Buenos Aires went delirious with joy on hearing the outcome of the Conference. The young Paraguayan General was paraded through the streets of the Capital in an open carriage. Flowers and confetti were showered on him and girls threw themselves at his feet. A military march was composed in his honour by Dalmiro Costa and played by every brass band in the city. And lastly the town of Buenos Aires presented him with an illuminated scroll. "Dedicated," as it said, "with due respect and in grateful thanks to his Most Excellent Senor Brigadier General don Francisco Solano Lopez, Minister Plenipotentiary of the Republic of Paraguay and saviour of Argentine blood, through whose friendly intervention we owe the satisfactory conclusion of the peace negotiations, a peace so whole-heartedly desired by our entire family."

It was at this precise moment that Mr. Edward Thornton, her Britannic Majesty's representative in Buenos Aires chose to strike.

Prior to returning home Francisco had bought, with an eye to business, the "Tacuari", a five hundred ton vessel which he had fitted out with valuable cargo. No sooner had he set sail with the Paraguayan flag waving in the breezes of the River Plate than Edward Thornton played his trump card. In defiance of the laws of nations, he ordered Admiral Lushington, Commander-in-Chief of the South Atlantic fleet* to send two men-of-war, aptly called "The Buzzard" and "The Grappler" to seize the Paraguayan ship. The Tacuari doubled back to port but was overtaken by the British and young Lopez was held as hostage for the life of Canstatt. This act of piracy on the part of the British obliged the President of Paraguay to release his prisoner. But by now the British Government was incensed and demanded indemnities before they would consent to give up their prize. Lopez was forced to comply but insisted that the terms should be kept secret to save his own face and pretend to his people that he had got the better of the British.

On the young General's eventual return to Asuncion he was hailed as a conquering hero and his father made him Minister of War. To avoid jealousy, and because he could do no less, he created his second son Benigno Commander in Chief of the Garrison at Asuncion and the third son was given the rank of Major in the Army, but not caring for the position he changed it for that of an Admiral of a non-existent fleet.

Soon Francisco was given the chance to win fresh laurels and was sent to Europe as Ambassador at large. He was instructed by his father to attract the attention of the world to Paraguay and to encourage emigration to the Chaco. At the

---

*The Royal Navy was under orders to patrol the coastal waters and the rivers in order to safeguard British interests and protect lives.

same time he was commissioned by the President to buy battleships from Queen Victoria.

With a tearful farewell from his mother and a salute of twenty one guns Francisco Solano set sail for Europe on Sunday, 12th June, 1853, on the "Independence of Paraguay".

CHAPTER SIX

A SOUTH AMERICAN IN PARIS

THE shrill cries of the Parisian newspaper vendors were muted by the shunting of locomotives and the ever recurring arrival and departure of trains. Passengers fought their way along the platforms of the Gare du Nord where fog and steam seemed to fuse and rise in vaporous waves to the domes of glass overhead reminiscent of the Crystal Palace.

In a recess of towering masonry Eliza Lynch stood holding her skirts about her to prevent them from trailing on the ground and disclosing layers of lilac petticoats like the petals of a flower. Her golden hair was partially hidden by a velvet hood. Two eyes, the colour of French enamel, shone with an azure light making the grim railway station appear less formidable. Only the clearcut lines of her jaw in an otherwise angelic face revealed an inner hardness. "Eliza, Eliza. You will be rich beyond the dreams of avarice." The voice of Satan whispered in her ear. Satan materialized in the shape of Juan Jose Brizuela, the young Charge d'Affaires at the Paraguayan Legation who supplemented his income by pimping.

He darted about the station like a ferret. "The train is late. Perhaps the Channel steamer was delayed because of the November fog. Do not forget I expect a commission." At that moment two lights like the eyes of a hunted animal emerged through the fog and the train came to a standstill with the grinding of brakes, the hissing of steam and a series of jerks. The young Charge d'Affaires pinched Eliza on the arm and said "Wait for me here. I will go and look for him."

Among the last to alight from a first class carriage was a small, thickset man with bandy legs who gazed around him with a proud disdainful look. Francisco possessed none of his

father's coarseness of features. The young General had a good
profile and wore his jet black beard neatly trimmed. Except
for the swarthiness of his complexion, he was not unlike the
Prince of Wales.

On the heels of Francisco Solano came his entourage don
Juan Andres Jelly, Jose Maria Aguiar, Vincente Barus and
Paulino Alen, all of them shivering in their light overcoats.
Their yellowish Indian complexions looked green in the dim
light of the station.

"A sus ordenes, mi General," Brizuela greeted his master.

The Ambassador-at-large condescendingly held out a hand
which the other grasped in both his own. "Senor, I welcome
you to Paris. Arrangements have been made for you to stay
at the newly-opened Hotel Continental. I trust you will find
it to your liking."

"I am satisfied that you have obeyed my father's instructions. I wish to meet the Emperor and Empress." Francisco
made no mention of the snub he had received at Osborne.
Queen Victoria had not been "at home." It was a slight that
he would never forget. He had retaliated by cancelling the
purchase of two Battlehips from Britain and placing the order
with the United States instead. But now his immediate concern was France. "My august father has requested me to inform his Majesty that we have room for French emigrés in the
Chaco and we will provide them with land in return for
cultivating the soil. Should they prove satisfactory they will
be given the status of citizens after five years." Then lowering
his tone he proceeded, "Did you get the confidential message
I sent you from London? I need the companionship of a
beautiful woman during my stay in Paris."

"She is here at the station, Senor."

Francisco was taken aback by the promptness of the
attaché's answer. The General gave him a searching look and
made up his mind that a man who could carry out such an
unsavoury task with so much aplomb was not be trusted. "You
have done well," he said. There was plenty of time to settle
the score later on—and not as the young man expected.

Brizuela led the way towards the exodus, threading his way in and out of the crowd, followed at a sedate distance by the son of the Dictator of Paraguay.

Suddenly, before them, Eliza Lynch stood revealed in the gaslight, illuminated by the yellow beams that infiltrated the fog. There was the fragrance of violets about her and the aura of the Empress she tried to emulate.

"Don Francisco, may I present Madame Lynch."

Eliza extended a gloved hand. At first glance he appeared pliable and easy going she thought but there was something about his eyes that disquietened her. Instinct warned her to proceed with caution.

"Welcome to Paris, Monsieur."

"It is kind of you to greet me."

He takes himself too seriously, Eliza thought, and has an inflated idea of his own importance.

At this moment Francisco's travelling companions herded together like sheep, approached the head of the mission.

Francisco Solano waved them aside angrily, "Can you not see that I am busy. Proceed to the hotel and wait upon me in the morning."

Hustled by blue smocked porters, newspaper vendors and sellers of lottery tickets, the small frightened figures were engulfed in the crowd.

"How small he is," thought Eliza, "but strong as a bull."

He, too, was undressing her in his imagination and brooding on future delights. While Eliza and the visitor to Paris exchanged formalities the young attaché summonded a cab and motioned Francisco Solano to step inside. The luggage was piled high on top, the coachman lashed his whip, the horses began to trot and Francisco fell back on the padded seats of the fiacre by the side of the saturnine attaché. "Wait, wait. Is she not coming with us?" Francisco looked out of the steamy windows and saw the figure of Eliza Lynch rapidly receding in a gauze of mist. Francisco's eyes gleamed with hatred. He had one more score to settle with Brizuela.

"I thought she was a woman of the streets."

"It is hard to explain Parisian society, senor. Her uncle is a bishop."

CHAPTER SEVEN

ELIZA ELOISA LYNCH

IN a document published in Buenos Aires in 1875 under the heading "Exposicion Protesta" Eliza Lynch declared "I was born in Ireland in 1835 of highly respectable parents, members of an old Anglo-Irish family. On my father's side I am related to several worthy Bishops and more than sixty Magistrates and through my mother I can claim connection with a Vice-Admiral who together with his two brothers fought with Nelson at the battle of Trafalgar. My family have always held high posts in Ireland." Yet it availed them nothing that they could claim a couple of Bishops and a score of Judges among their ancestors. The Lynchs were impoverished, being landed gentry without land. Eliza's parents were a happy-go-lucky charming and utterly irresponsible couple. As time went on it was imperative that Eliza's father should seek a livelihood to support his family. But what to do? and how to set about it? He was unqualified in the few professions that were open to a man of his class at the time such as the State, Medicine or Law.

Eliza's two brothers, ten years older than herself, held commissions in Her Majesty's navy and her elder sister had married a French musician and had gone to live in Paris. Consequently, because of the disparity in age, she was brought up as an only child.

Looking back across the years Eliza could never forget the famine of '45. It had left its mark. It was as if she had been branded for the rest of her life. Ten years old at the time, she had witnessed scenes that had remained indelibly printed in her mind. Her chief recollection was one of hunger, a gnawing, lightheaded nausea that ate into her very vitals and

made her vomit with emptiness. The potato harvest had
failed. For seven years it was to fail but this was the first time
within living memory and therefore the most bewildering.
Even if they had had the means it would have been impossible
to buy food. The shops were empty. Relief committees had
been set up in Cork but they were forced to close after a few
days as supplies ran out. Eliza, listlessly playing with her toys
in the nursery, could hear her parents wrangling in the next
room. How well she remembered her mother trying to make
a stew with a handful of roots dug out of the garden; and she
still had visions of her father lifting a glass of whisky to his
lips and his exclamations when, far from relieving the void,
the alcohol had only accentuated the burning hunger. The
servants had long since disappeared to scavenge for themselves in the country districts.

Then there was the night when Eliza, crying with distress,
had been dressed hurriedly. With true Irish improvidence
her parents had just abandoned the house. Corinne, Eliza's
sister had written from Paris suggesting that they come and
stay with her during the present crisis and pool their
resources. The idea had taken root and John Lynch had decided that rather than face starvation in Cork he would collect
every penny that he could lay hands on and take his wife and
youngest child to France where he hoped to retrieve his vanished fortunes in the mad gold rush of the Second Empire.

They made their way to the harbour. The child walked
with quick steps trying to keep up with her parents. Soon
they were out of the better part of the town and walking past
rows of windowless mud huts. Hungry, menacing crowds had
collected in the mean streets demanding food or work. The
wind blew from the East bringing with it the stench of rotting
potatoes. It was estimated that three and a half million pounds
of the staple diet of the people had perished. Many unfortunate peasants were reduced to eating their own excrement
mixed with cabbage leaves. Mr. Nicholas Cummins, J.P.
wrote to Sir Charles Trevelyan at the Treasury: "The alarm-
ing prospect cannot be exaggerated. In the whole of the city

and port of Cork there is only four thousand tons of food stuff.
Unless great amounts reach us from other quarters, the prospect is appalling. I assure you that unless something is immediately done the people must die . . ." This fate John
Lynch was determined to prevent and had booked passages
for his reduced family on the packet boat for Le Havre. They
crept on board like fugitives and were glad enough to reach
the comparative safety of the deck. But while the vessel was
still in harbour rumour spread that despite the fact that Ireland was starving the Government was exporting oats to
England. The demented population ran to the landing stage
"Curses be on the English who are leaving us to starve." Past
the wharfs and warehouses they swarmed, emerging like rats
from all directions intent on plunder, loot or murder. More
than four hundred men and women thronged the quay.
Veterans with wooden legs, scarecrows and hags were out for
blood. Some carried torches, others held banners that waved
limply in the drizzle and there were others still armed with
wooden ploughs, the only weapons at their command. On they
came shouting obscenities. The ship sounded her sirens, short
plaintive blasts that echoed in the oily darkness of the bay.
The Captain intent on getting under way ordered the stokers
to get up steam. The little girl stood on deck between her
parents who tried to shield her with their arms from the sight.
Eliza wore a long coat with a fur tippet and carried a muff.
Her mother was draped in a short pelisse and her father
sported an Ulster and a Glengarry cap. They were not unlike
hundreds of other fleeing refugees.

The maddened crowd in an effort to restrain the ship from
sailing grabbed the moorings and tried to hold her back with
their bare hands. As the vessel hove to the more nimble among
them endeavoured to scale up the side of the ship and jump
aboard. Several fell into the water. A sharp cry and an
ominous splash ended their frantic bid for retribution. They
were oblivious to pain, danger or death. The ten-year-old
child saw murder written in the eyes of her countrymen. A
maniac, lusting for blood, rushed towards her parents intent

on killing them, and fell dead at their feet, causing the superstitious Irish to draw back in horror. The face of the dead man
had a sobering effect and the mob crawled away like dogs and
stood about on deck awaiting their punishment. They were
rowed back to land in an open boat to face the famine and
the ship proceeded on her way to France.

But in spite of their high hopes the lights of Paris did not
shine too brightly on Eliza's parents. John Lynch may have
had a glib tongue but the investments that he made on the
bourse were more speculative than shrewd. Besides they found
to their consternation that Corinne, who had been urging
them to join her was not as affluent as she had led them to
expect and far from living in luxury they had to support their
elder daughter as well as her musician husband. They lived
a hand-to-mouth existence. It was no small wonder, therefore
that when Eliza, at the age of fourteen, declared her intentions
of marrying a veterinary surgeon by the name of Quatrefages,
the parents raised no objection. In fact they were relieved to
find someone willing to take their daughter off their hands
without a dowry. Eliza was tall for her age and showed promise of great beauty to come but her most striking characteristic, even at that age, was her iron determination. When
the French put certain difficulties in the way of her marriage
by declaring that she was not of age, that she had not been
received into the Roman Catholic church and that she must
wait until she was sixteen, she brushed all obstacles aside and
insisted on being married in England. With the same Irish
improvidence that had driven them across the channel, they
returned to England and stayed with Mrs. Lynch's sister who
was married to Commander William Royle Clarke of the
British Navy.

The wedding took place on 3rd June, 1850 at Folkstone
Parish Church according to the rites of the established
Church, being solemnized by the Reverend Thomas Pearce.
Eliza tells us in her Confessions "I was married in England on
the 3rd June, 1850, to M. Quatrefages now (1875) holding a
high ranking position in France. I lived with my husband

for two years, residing both in France and in Algiers but had no children by him." If Eliza had only realized the disastrous repercussions that marriage was to have she would never have embarked on it.

Within two years Eliza was bored. She was bored with the provincial life of a Garrison town in North Africa and bored with the restricted duties imposed on the wife of a Veterinary Surgeon attached to a cavalry Regiment. Eliza cold-bloodedly and without any recriminations left her husband and returned to France only to find that her father had died during her absence and her mother had returned to Ireland.

Rather than face a life of genteel poverty in Cork she decided to remain in Paris. Ireland meant to her famine, hunger and poverty. If starve she must, she would starve in Paris. There and then she made up her mind to sell herself. But her true nature asserting itself she decided to place a high price on her favours. For a short time she shared the Bohemian quarters of her sister but was soon installed in an opulent apartment where she had a marble bathroom with silver fittings that looked like the Sacristy of a Church.

Eliza never lacked admirers who fought for the privilege of paying her rent. Notwithstanding she realized with a wisdom beyond her years that her youth and beauty would not last forever and she began to look around for a rich foreigner who might become her permanent protector. Paris was the place to find him. Here came the millionaires to parade their wealth. Suitors were easy to ensnare for a night but hard to engulf for a lifetime. Eliza dispersed her agents throughout the city and left cards at the principal hotels and Embassies describing herself as an instructress of languages.

In the rare moments that Eliza thought of her mother her conscience troubled her but, she reasoned, there was all the difference in the world between being a cheap cocotte and a demi-mondaine. It was in this underworld of Offenbach, more glittering than the Society it imitated, that Eliza Lynch held sway. But her friendships were not confined to the Bohemian circles of Hortense Schneider, Cora Pearl and their like but

extended to the old and new nobility including Matilde Bonaparte, the daughter of King Jerome who seemed to prefer the
society of courtesans to the straight laced ladies of Eugenie's
court. There was not a gala at the Opera or the Opera Bouffe
that Eliza superbly dressed, did not attend either alone or
escorted by some aspirant to her favours.

Quick to take advantage of temporary wealth, Eliza had
installed a salon where she presided over a gaming table.
The estranged wife of a Veterinary Surgeon was shrewd
enough not to play for high stakes but preferred to control
the bank and pocket whatever came her way in the nature of
pourboires for the house. Night after night she sat at the baize
topped table feigning an interest in the game about her while
her thoughts dwelt on the South American diplomat. According to the flip of a card people won and lost thousands but the
stakes she played for involved a South American State.

Meanwhile the Ambassador Extraordinary to the Courts
of St. James and St. Louis had good reason to be pleased with
his visit to France. He found the people more sympathetic
than the British who, he decided, were an ignorant race and
had no idea that his country was even placed on the map.
Here, on the contrary, he was on excellent terms with the
Rothschilds as well as the famous financiers John and Alfred
Blyth who were willing to act as his agents in exchange for the
monopoly of the yerba trade in Europe.

Before calling on the Emperor and Empress, Francisco was
determined to have a uniform made worthy of the occasion.
Accordingly, he went to de Paule the military tailor by
appointment to Napoleon to have a uniform executed to his
own design (costing 525 francs) with such a galaxy of gold
lace that he was one of the first South American Generals to
be dubbed 'Rastaquoèves.'* Francisco was gratified to make
the acquaintance of Bonaparte's nephew. Had not Napoleon
been his childhood dream? He glowed with self importance

*Cunningham-Graham states: "In those days the word 'rastaquoève'
was not invented, but as there were strong men before Agamemnon, so
there were rastaquoèves before the Palais Royal Theatre had made the
name generic for all South Americans.

as he was conducted down a long series of connecting drawing rooms, the doors of which were flung open by liveried servants. The Emperor stood behind an ormulu desk to receive him and he was not alone. He was accompanied by the Empress who made herself charming and spoke to him in her native Spanish. Francisco was dazzled by the magnificence of the court and the beauty of Eugenie. He bowed and presented the Emperor with a hundred boxes of the best Paraguayan cigars and a sample of tobacco which Louis Napoleon promised to exhibit in the 1854 Paris Exhibition and which in fact won first prize. He had no difficulty in concluding a treaty whereby five hundred emigrants were to be sent as Colonizers to a corner of the Chaco but recently renamed Nueva Burdeos, in exchange for a grant of land. General Lopez kissed the Empress's hand and the Emperor personally conducted him to the door of his study and dismissed him with the words "J'éspère que vous vous amusez à Paris, Monsieur," and entrusted an equerry with the task of seeing that the young General's stay in the French capital should be made agreeable. As he took his leave the Emperor kissed him on both cheeks and presented him with the Legion of Honour. Francisco's bosom swelled with pride and he was filled with the ambition of becoming the Napoleon of the New World.

Two nights later Francisco was taken to Madame Lynch's salon and to his surprise he saw the woman he had met at the Gare du Nord seated at a green baize table. She was reflected in a pool of gaslight that threw the rest of the room in shadows. Her fair hair glistened like gold and the moulded bosoms resembled a couple of sunflowers that were about to burst over the garden wall of her dress. She could well have been an angel that had strayed from Heaven by mistake and stepped into a gambling den to rub shoulders with flâneurs, entrepreneurs, hunchbacks, dwarfs and duennas in an orgy of self destruction.

Eliza hardly recognized the stranger that stood before her resplendent in gold epaulettes, cordons and stripes. He had just come from a sitting with David, the artist. Defiantly he threw a handful of gold on the table. With a spontaneous desire to protect him she made an involuntary movement but the gesture merely served to provoke him to double his original stakes. The shoe was passed from one player to another and speedily relinquished. Three times running, Francisco played against the bank, each time leaving his accumulated winnings on the table and three times he was successful. Then with an imperious air, he passed over the pile of louis d'or to Eliza who thanked him haughtily, placed the money in a beaded bag and arose majestically from the table. Eliza led him towards a Louis XVI settee. She took stock of her intended lover and was not slow to sum him up. The only way to dominate this half-tamed savage is through flattery, she thought. He was vain, ignorant and gullible but beneath it all there was an Indian shrewdness. Eliza made full use of his weaknesses and complimented him on the fine military figure he cut. To which he replied without any undue modesty, " I proved my military ability when I was called upon to arbitrate between the boundaries of the Argentine and Banda Oriental. This feat alone established my fame and made me the natural successor of my father when he be called to join the Almighty. An event I pray does not happen for many a long year." He made it sound as if don Carlos would be invited to help God govern the Universe. To make up for his lack of stature he strutted round the room like a young peacock. When asked what he thought of Paris he pretended to be unimpressed by the sights. "There is nothing like my own country," he boasted, "We have sunshine and we have space." In truth he was a little God in Paraguay and resented the fact that he was nobody in Europe.

Towards morning, when the last gamblers had taken their leave Eliza allowed him to accompany her as far as her boudoir. In spite of himself, he was impressed by the rich hangings, the marbletopped tables, the petit point, the pompoms, the French fireplace and the Aubusson carpet but his interest soon gave way to impatience. "Are you not going to dismiss your maid?"

"I would not trust myself to be alone with you, Sir, without a chaperone."

He was somewhat mollified by the prompt reply and laughed harshly.

Eliza ordered the grisette to bring a bottle of champagne. She must be shrewd and not give herself too easily. If everything he told her was true there was untold wealth in Paraguay. Eliza was an adventuress in more ways than one. She was willing to take a far bigger gamble than any game of chemin-de-fer and if she won, she would be a pioneer in a field that was yet to be explored. Let the Hortense Schneiders of this world have the mansions, the carriages and jewels and spend the wealth of their admirers as they squandered their own lives. Eliza Lynch would conquer Virgin lands. From the first she had made up her mind to accompany this stranger to the ends of the world or rather the New World. She asked a dozen questions. "What is the population of Asuncion? What are the natural resources? In what provinces are minerals to be found? What was the percentage of Spanish compared to Guarani?" He readily expanded on his favourite subject but every time he tried to take her in his arms the *bonne* hovered in the background. Francisco made no effort to conceal his annoyance; Eliza merely laughed and they talked until the crystal chandeliers became dim in the dawn and he returned to the hotel strangely elated, but unsatisfied, with the strains of the waltz from "La Belle Helene" ringing in his ears.

One week later Eliza Lynch became the mistress of General Lopez. Francisco wrote to his father that he was attending scientific lectures in Paris but in reality he was strutting up and down the Rue de Rivoli by the side of Eliza's carriage which was filled with purchases of every description varying in size from five carat diamonds to crinolines. The young General was completely spellbound. Eliza was everything that he most admired, the epitome of luxury, elegance and culture. He was not sufficiently au fait with the intricacies of Society to know that the world she represented was the underworld.

In his eyes she was a great lady and if in the past her morals had been elastic, how many ladies of Asuncion were above reproach. Hand in hand Francisco and Eliza paid their respects to the great Napoleon and gazed in wonder not unmixed with envy on his tomb at the Invalides.

They set out on a grand tour of Europe, combining the delights of a honeymoon with pleasures of broadening the mind. They visited Spain and were received by Isabella II and her Minister for Foreign Affairs don Angel Calderon de la Barca. The Queen was undiplomatic and caused considerable annoyance to the son of the Dictator of Paraguay by suggesting that as his country had once been a Colony of Spain its citizens should be allowed to choose between Spanish or Paraguayan nationality. The indignant General and Madame Lynch proceeded to Caserta where they enjoyed the hospitality of the King of the two Sicilies who invested Francisco with the order of St. Maurice and St. Lazare. There followed a short wisit to Rome where they bought their table silver. From there the enraptured couple ventured as far as the Crimea to inspect the fortifications where the Paraguayan General, who had never been under fire, and his Irish mistress must have seemed bizarre.

When the time came for Francisco to return to Asuncion he decided that, despite the technical difficulty that there was a husband in the background, he could not live without her. On being asked to accompany him to Paraguay, Eliza is reputed to have said "Might there not be a revolution, Sir?" To which he replied "In Paraguay, we have no revolutions, Madame, unless it be your beauty that provokes one."

The cranes of the Tacuari, which had been sent to escort him home, strained and screeched, loading cases of furniture, carriages and cabin trunks filled with lingerie and dresses more in keeping for Baden Baden than Asuncion, not to mention uniforms designed for the General to wear on every occasion and one hundred and forty patent leather boots.

Before leaving Europe Francisco enlisted the services of engineers, medical men, chemists, professional soldiers and agriculturists to whom he gave a five year contract on the understanding that half their salaries would be paid in the currency of the country and the other half in gold. He wanted Paraguay to be the most up to date country in South America and the most powerful and made arrangements for these experts to follow at the earliest opportunity. Francisco and Eliza sailed from Bordeaux at ten thirty in the morning on 11th of November, 1854.

Eliza sat on deck wrapped in a cashmere shawl. Her blue Irish eyes sparkled to see the coast of Europe recede. She had no misgivings but was filled with a great exultation for the future. This dark foreigner who stood by her side, and boasted all day long of the glories of his country, was no longer a stranger but the father of her unborn child. Francisco was passionate, sensuous and insatiable while she feigned a passion that she far from felt. But, she was content. Her very lack of emotion was her strength. While she gazed at the ocean, trying to see beyond the horizon, Francisco Solano paced up and down the deck dreaming of conquests, a thirst for domination, aflame with ambition. He was building castles in the air which, if he but knew it, were no less grandiose than hers. "South America is large," Eliza was thinking. "Brazil is an empire. Paraguay is larger than France. Francisco Solano is the son of the President. Presidents do not last forever; and then?"

CHAPTER EIGHT

ASUNCION

THE old Tacuari wheezed its way up the Paraguay, a thousand miles of navigable river that runs from Montevideo to Asuncion. At Paso de la Patria, a Paraguayan pilot boarded the ship. He sat cross-legged on the bridge and gave his orders in nasal Guarani. Skillfully, he guided the paddle boat through the currents and avoided the "Camelotes" floating islands of water lilies. "Jacares", alligators lay on the sand banks pretending to be logs of wood. Toucans flitted by the side of the deck, looking like gigantic kingfishers. Herons, with open beaks, hovered low over the muddy water hoping to catch a flying fish. Eliza, reclining beneath an awning, sailed through a breathless world and watched an occasional hamlet drift by, nestling against a crop of stunted palm trees, or an island, set mid-stream, feathered with bamboo and bulrushes, while beyond, to the left lay the mysterious Gran Chaco, an uncharted desert of wasteland and lagoons roamed over by tribes of semi-wild Indians on horseback, adorned with tufts of ostrich feathers and carrying long spears, who from time to time would sweep down on their neighbours with a wild war-cry.

As the paddle steamer drifted past the hills of Lambare, on the 21st January, 1855, Francisco, bursting with suppressed emotion, joined Eliza on deck. Asuncion lay before them. Eliza could see one-storey adobe houses with tiled roofs, the same colour as the blood red earth of Paraguay stretching along endless shadeless streets. No effort had been made to level the town nor did it follow any set pattern. The buildings rested on the topographical contours of the uneven slopes. Thus the foundation of one house was built on a level with

43

the roof of the next. The customs house, the Cabildo, Francia's Palace and the colonnaded hospital encompassed the great market square, as soulless as a drilling ground, which swept down to the water's edge. Persons of both sexes wore the coarse white linen garment of the country and walked barefoot. Women brought their wares to market in huge baskets which they carried on their heads. To Eliza they looked like figures in a frieze of an Etruscan vase. The goods were laid out on the ground under hastily erected stalls, more in the nature of tents, beside which their owner squatted, smoking large cigars, and passed the day, bargaining in a sing song voice, over the price of yams, maize and mandioca. The tinny clang of church bells rung from the Colonial belfry of an immense worm-eaten Cathedral announced the mid-day hour. From the decks of the steamer the bustling movement in the town looked like the activity of ants.

As soon as the Tacuari dropped anchor the news spread mysteriously throughout Asuncion that Francisco Solano was on board. The inhabitants, semi-Spaniard, semi-Guarani, left their houses and came running from all directions. Pyramids of pumpkins and watermelons, baskets of persimmons and prickly pears were abandoned; sellers and bargain hunters abruptly ceased their haggling and surged towards the landing stage.

To their surprise, instead of seeing their General in a habitual uniform or wearing his well-known poncho they beheld him looking over the side of the ship, attired in a blue frock coat, a monumental top hat and tight fitting trousers strapped over high heeled boots.

"Taita Guazu" Great Lord. Caria Gauzu. Big Lord. A great shout rent the air. The populace yelled and clapped their hands like children. One or two daredevils jumped into the water and swam out to the Tacuari in spite of the alligators that were apt to bite off a limb. The spectators neither applauded nor encouraged these antics but looked on with true Indian fatalism.

Paraguay may have been more primitive than Eliza was

led to expect but she could not deny that Francisco Solano was almost a God in the people's eyes and the child that lay within her would unite them closer than any legal marriage. At that moment the population seemed to become aware of Eliza who stood beside the General holding a parasol in her hands. Far from voicing another mighty acclamation their jaws opened in astonishment. They had never before seen a woman with golden hair and blue eyes. Madame Lynch was wearing a dress the colour of pale lilac with a bonnet to match and a lace stole which hid her figure. The simplest Guarani thought that she was an apparition from heaven come to visit them and knelt in reverence along the water front. *Little did they know that for most of them she would turn out to be an angel of death.*

Eliza picked up her skirts and followed Francisco down the gangway. Two dark skinny arms belonging to the oarsman helped her to jump on to the canoe which conveyed them swiftly to the wooden landing stage, the steps of which graduated to the river and were exposed to a greater or lesser extent according to the tide. Francisco escorted his mistress ashore and led her through reverential crowds towards a group of carriages not unlike black marias that stood by the side of the Customs House. A number of horses were held by orderlies while the Presidential guard stood about in groups waiting for a word of command to resume their escort duty. In the first carriage sat a fat elderly gentleman. His dimensions were such that he occupied the whole of the back seat. He held his sword across his knees as if it were a walking stick. This was don Carlos Antonio Lopez, Dictator of Paraguay.

Francisco jauntily strode up to his father and presented Madame Lynch. It was the first intimation that the old gentleman had received that his son had imported a mistress as well as a uniform from Paris. Eliza advanced towards him with a radiant smile and held out a gloved hand but the old Dictator barely acknowledged her presence and with a curt nod of the head gave the signal to the coachman to proceed.

There followed a quick word of command, the escort mounted their horses and trotted behind the carriage raising clouds of dust.

The colour of Francisco's skin, which turned an olive green was the only sign of his displeasure. Without saying a word, he took Eliza by the hand and walked towards the second carriage occupied by dona Juana Pabla Carillo and her daughters Inocenia and Rafaela. The three ladies were equally corpulent and their black dresses were stained with sweat under their armpits. Francisco introduced Madame Lynch to his mother and to his sisters but they merely looked through her, and the Senora Presidenta told the coachman to go home "A casa" which he did too precipitously, causing Eliza's dress to be splattered with excrement. A third carriage stood by with its springs sagging under the weight of Benigno and Venancio who bulged out of their tropical suits as they lolled back on the padded seats of the coach. They did not even wait for Francisco to come up to them but gave the orders to proceed and departed smirking.

CHAPTER NINE

THE RETURN OF THE PRODIGAL SON

WITH excessive pride Francisco presented Eliza with a house in the Calle Independencia. As she walked through the massive doorway studded with silver nails her heart was filled with dismay. It was a one storey mansion built around an inner courtyard and occupied a whole block. The thick adobe walls were inserted with barred windows that overlooked the street. The rooms were unconnected; each one having a life-size door that gave immediate access into the patio, making it necessary to step into the open when passing from one room into another. In the centre of the patio stood a well surrounded by a cluster of orange trees planted in no set formation. In certain seasons the ground was baked like an oven and at others exuded a moisture that rose from the damp sodden earth. Across the courtyard were the kitchen quarters, recognizable by their smell and the chickens that scampered in the vicinity. A gnarled old woman whose face was half eaten away by leprosy showed them around the house unlocking and unbarring doors. Francisco told her in Guarani that dona Eliza was now the mistress of the house and that her orders must be obeyed as implicitly as if they were his own. Leaving Eliza in the care of the leper Francisco rode off to see his parents. "Do not wait up for me. I may be late." His jaw stuck out and his expression was resolute.

Half an hour later Francisco stormed into the palace. He shouted at his father, railed his mother, intimidated his brothers and bullied his sisters. "I will resign from the army," he thundered. "I will leave the country for once and for all. You do not appreciate me. Try and get along without me."

"Why could you not have chosen a girl from Asuncion," whined his mother.

"She is a great lady. I will marry her one day when her husband gives her a divorce."

Dona Juana sat on a horse-hair settee and wept into a black edged handkerchief. Mourning had become a habit for her. The Senora Presidenta kept repeating "Nothing will ever make me accept that woman." But Francisco was more interested in seeing Paraguay the strongest state in South America than concerned whether or not his mother would receive Madame Lynch. "We must install a large military camp at Cerro Leon and organise the finest army in South America. We must invite Prussian instructors to train the army. We must construct more docks, extend the railways, encourage emigration." Francisco's enthusiasm was contagious.

In spite of his indiscretion in bringing Madame Lynch to Paraguay the old Dictator was pleased to be reunited with his son. Now seeing him, old Lopez realised how dull life had been during Francisco's absence in Europe. He was the one person to whom he could talk, the one person who had vision, who understood his motives. Benigno and Venancio were mere sycophants, bloated ne'er do wells. Don Carlos questioned Francisco about the engineers, agriculturalists and doctors to whom he had given contracts, about the French emigrants to the Chaco. What did they think of Paraguay in the outside world? "Are the French as grasping as they are made out to be? Is it true that the English are a Nation of shopkeepers?" They talked far into the night long after the other members of the family had retired. Don Carlos was getting old and kept repeating, "I rely on you".

Francisco came away from the interview well satisfied that he was his father's right hand man. He was entrusted by his Excellency with ample powers to carry out the most expansive programme in the history of Paraguay. In one respect only was the Dictator adamant. Neither he nor his family would receive Madame Lynch.

"Is there no way of getting rid of her," said the Senora Presidenta as she wished her husband good night.

"Only through murder," answered the Dictator sleepily.

"There is no such thing as murder in Paraguay," wheezed the old lady asthmatically. "All deaths come from natural causes."

CHAPTER TEN

A NEW COUNTRY

ELIZA was glad to be alone and free of Francisco's disquieting presence for a while. She dismissed the leper woman and examined her surroundings. For some unaccountable reason she had taken a dislike to the house. She was not given to brooding but she felt apprehensive. In the torrid twilight, as the day vanished with the quick even tempo of an hourglass, she sat listening to the chatter of the servants, the buzz of the insects and the tinny clang of the church bells rung from the Cathedral de la Encarnacion. A melancholy sweetness overcame her. She was intrepidly fearless, yet she was seized with a strange suffocating sense of doom like the gathering of a storm, both oppressive and exciting. Here she was, an Anglo-Irish woman, hardly more than a girl sitting in a garden in Asuncion, the mistress of the son of the Dictator of Paraguay, a thousand miles from Buenos Aires, seven thousand miles from Europe, without a friend in the world and only protected by an unpredictable Paraguayan. If she had not much imagination she had immense confidence in herself which served her equally well.

Eliza clapped her hands. At once a dozen servants ran to do her bidding. They wore gold ear-rings, amulets and bracelets causing them to jingle as they ran like a team of pack animals. It was impossible to tell which were servants and which were liberated slaves but in truth there was little difference between the two for the majority had refused their freedom, deeply hurt that their masters should even contemplate such a step. It was a patriarchal system whereby they felt they belonged to the same family as their owners, sharing their sorrows and their joys, and if the overlords had the greater privileges they also had the greater responsibilities.

With a few words of Spanish and a demonstration of mime Eliza made them understand that she wished to be served dinner. Lightheartedly they ran backwards and forwards to the kitchen and prceeded to lay a table in the garden and served her with soup, a carbonada, a stew of mutton and mandioca and a variety of fruit including custard apples and prickly pears. The meal was adequate if not princely. As she ate, the servants crept out of the house with true Indian stealth and made a ring around her. They stood unseen, hiding in the shadows of the night. Like children, they watched her spellbound. To them she was like an apparition from another world. A more perceptive person might have sensed their presence but Eliza was too practical to feel an atmosphere. Long before midnight she arose from the table and retired to her room. Her path was illuminated by hundreds of fireflies that flickered in the tropical night. She undressed by the dim light of a candle that cast its lugubrious shadows on the uninviting room showing patches of damp on the bare walls. A silver jug and ewer reposed on a Victorian washstand and a marble topped commode stood nearby. One or two vaulted leather trunks lay open but as yet unpacked and only her immediate necessities had been put out for the night and placed on a large massive bedstead behind which hung a crucifix made of fibre, a souvenir of Palm Sunday. Eliza was more quick to notice that the mattress sagged in the middle and that the floor boards creaked underfoot as she prepared herself for bed.

One by one she blew out the candles and crept under the mosquito net. But whether it was the oppressive heat or the excitement of the long day, sleep eluded her and she tossed and turned waiting for Francisco to join her. She was on the point of dozing when she heard a blood curdling scream followed by the sounds of blows and what appeared to be the stampede of rats. She lay perfectly still, afraid to move. There it was again. Cackling hollow laughter and renewed thumps penetrated the adobe wall. Was this a joke? Was it somebody in distress? Or was it a conspiracy to get rid of her perpetrated by a jealous rival?

In spite of her already cumbersome figure she got out of bed and turned the handle in an effort to leave the room and learn the cause of the disturbance. To her utter amazement she found that the door was locked. Furiously she hammered on the unyielding portals but no one responded. Yet the hair-raising screams, scuffles and stampedes continued as if emerging from the next room. Unable to get any response to her knocks she ran to the window only to find herself confronted by iron bars. The night was dark and airless. Not a soul stirred. Asuncion was like a city of the dead except for the disturbances around her. Then from her position, behind the grille, she saw a reassuring sight. A night watchman carrying a lantern stood at the street corner. "Two o'clock in the morning and all serene." She called out to him in a torrent of English, French and Spanish. The man looked up at the window and gaped. In his fright he dropped the lantern and and ran down the street as if pursued by a thousand demons. The louder she shouted the quicker he ran and every effort on her part was re-echoed in a cacophony of sound as if unseen forces jeered at her from every angle. Eliza felt impotent with rage and was too unnerved to get back to bed and spent the night sitting on an upright chair waiting for Francisco to return. She had no idea how long she sat or how long she waited but towards morning she fell into a doze. When at length Francisco arrived he was met with a torrent of abuse. "How dare you lock me in? Whose orders are they? Am I a prisoner? Am I not a free Englishwoman? I will return to Europe."

Francisco was clearly taken aback. He could not make out what had happened. Then he realised. The house in the Calle Independencia stood next to the Prison and the sounds that Eliza heard were those of the prisoners in their cells. It was obvious that the servants, in all good faith had locked the doors to protect Eliza from being raped in case the prisoners escaped. This was the kind of joke that appealed to Francisco and he laughed until the tears ran down his face. But Eliza did not have the same sense of humour. "I will not stay in this house one moment longer than necessary. You might at least have warned me. You must build me a new house." In a rage she crept between the sheets and turned her back on him. He was still laughing when he joined her. They lay side by side endeavouring to sleep but soon they discovered that they were not the only occupants of the bed. They shared the couch with an army of bed bugs that gave them little rest. Francisco's laughter turned to a raging bellow and it was Eliza's turn to calm him down.

CHAPTER ELEVEN

SETTLING DOWN

FROM the first she used her influence to embellish Asuncion. Mr. Taylor, the English Master Builder, one of the many craftsmen invited to Paraguay, was commissioned to erect an Opera House on the lines of the Scala at Milan. A Palace was designed that stretched along the water front, no whit inferior to Versailles; the foundations were of freestone, brought from a place called "Empedoado", but stuccoed to look like stone. Not content with these public buildings, they made plans for a library, a new post office and a grand social club. Money was no object. Francisco had carte blanche from his father to develop the country in every conceivable way. As the majority of the male population were conscripted, slave labour and boys, not yet ten, carried stones and worked day and night to complete this grandiose scheme.

Mr. Washburn, the United States minister at Asuncion at the time, wrote a history of Paraguay in which he relates, "It was a sad sight to see the little fellows made prematurely old by the labour to which they were condemned. They were constantly watched and in passing through the grounds where they wrought, they appeared like worn-out slaves in whom all hope was so utterly extinguished that they never looked up or ceased for a moment in their labours." Mr. Washburn goes on to say, "They were scantily fed. The poor little wretches were only allowed six or eight cents a day to buy their food."

As soon as the carriages were uncrated, Eliza went out for a drive in her English dog cart. Francisco gallantly rode by her side pointing out the sights of his native city with a feeling of possession. Beyond the town they came to a great open

plain called the Campo Grande where race meetings were
held every Sunday. The stunted tropical vegitation had been
levelled over to make a hippodrome. It was the rule of this
primitive sporting club that not more than two horses should
compete in the same race and it was stipulated that both
riders should use identical riding whips, a condition that
often served as an excuse for a false start as the jockeys would
accuse each other of failing to comply with the regulations.
In a paddock nearby stood a conglomeration of "ramadas"—
reed huts covered in awning where pedlars sold their wares
tortillas and the native brandy cana, to the onlookers.
Between races, the spectators drank and performed sarandigs
and pishesheshes, a shuffling dance so called because of the
hissing sound made with the toe of the foot. Eliza stood for
a long time watching the spectacle without saying a word.
Finally, Francisco grew impatient, "Well, Eliza, what do you
think?"

"Here," she said, "we will build a replica of Longchamps."

Shortly before the birth of her child, Eliza moved out of
the capital and settled at "Patino", a country quinta five
miles out of Asuncion. It was a pink and white marble Palace
built to her own design to which the natives gave the name
of "Madame Cué" meaning abode of the lady in Guarani.
Stone-masons worked day and night to complete the building.
All other work was temporarily suspended so that Francisco's
eldest son, or daughter, should be born in a setting worthy
of his or her rank. The house was one of the first in Paraguay
to be built on two floors. The centre block was like a child's
dolls house from which protruded two low parallel wings. A
vaulted carriageway, that penetrated the house from one side
to the other connected the outer with the inner patio where
two sweeping staircases rising in ornate curves met on a balustraded balcony that ran the length of the house and overlooked an orange grove set amongst canals and box hedges.
This was Eliza's favourite retreat where she spent most of
her time sewing, studying music, reading and learning

Spanish and Guarani. The new house with its exotic air and Empire furniture had a European air about it as if the Petit Trianon had been transplanted to La Recoleta. A newspaper article published at the time in Beunos Aires had the following to say. "Many of Madame Lynch's brasses and porcelains are museum pieces and the French tapestries and Oriental rugs are distributed with excellent taste and in a manner to delight the eye."

A straight road connected the capital with Madame Lynch's residence. This avenue was built in record time to enable Francisco to mount his horse at the Cabildo and be with his mistress within half an hour. The small estate included a corral where cows were kept and Eliza could play at being Marie Antoinette. Further afield there were plantations of maize and mandioca, patches of sweet potatoes and water melons, while dotted about the gentle rust coloured landscape there were reeds of bamboo sheltering the peones and liberated slaves who toiled on the blood-red earth of Paraguay.

To all outward appearance it was an earthly paradise yet Eliza was far from satisfied. From the first she had been utterly humiliated. She had come prepared to love and to be loved; instead she had been deeply wounded, The attitude of the President and his family, who lived close by, she could understand but that the foreign residents should persistently ignore her was a festering wound that refused to heal. Worst of all was the attitude of the old Spanish families who, despite broad hints from the General, treated her as if she were a whore and crossed themselves at the mere sight of her driving round the streets of Asuncion. The irony of her position was that these same people who scorned her did not possess one tenth of her breeding or cultivation.

The birth of her baby temporarily dispelled the tedium of life. Swansdown quilts were kicked aside by an olive skinned blue-eyed baby dressed in layers of lace made by the nuns of Asuncion. Although it was common knowledge that Francisco had three children by Juanita Pesoa as well as a little girl called Rosita Carreras, the birth of his eldest son by Madame Lynch was an event and aroused as much interest as that of a hereditary Crown Prince. In his capacity of Commander-in-Chief Francisco ordered a salute of a hundred and one guns. He was intent on having the child ostentatiously christened in the Cathedral but the old President refused to attend the ceremony and the Bishop of Asuncion, his Uncle Basilo, would not consent to baptise the infant born out of wedlock. For days Francisco seethed with rage and inwardly cursed both his father and his uncle but was powerless to enforce the measure. To save appearances he asked Father Palacios, a simple country priest with an ingratiating manner, to perform the ceremony in a private chapel of the Quinta. The child was named Francisco after his father but was always known as Panchito. Francisco doted on his son and would send for him on the slightest provocation to pet and spoil him.

No sooner had Eliza recovered her figure than she found herself pregnant again, a fact that infuriated her. She determined to ignore her condition and rode about the capital at a breakneck speed not caring whether she had a miscarriage or not. But nature, perverse in her way, held fast, and a second baby was born on August 6th, 1856, and christened Corinne Adelaide. She was given the name of Corinne after her sister and Adelaide after her mother. The new infant may have been an unwanted child but the moment she arrived Eliza was infatuated with her. It was therefore a cruel stroke of fate when the baby died six months later in February, 1857. For the first time in her life Eliza was distraught with grief. The child was dressed as an angel by wailing Guarani women who sewed a pair of gauze wings on to her frock and placed her in a small white coffin. In her sorrow Eliza wrote a poem. She had the words placed on her child's tombstone which stood, and still stands, on the left of the main entrance to the cemetry of La Recoleta immediately beside the mortuary chapel.

To the sacred Memory
of
Corrine Adelaide Lynch
Born August 6th, 1856
Died February 14th, 1857.

Ere sin could blight or sorrow fade
Death came with friendly care
The lovely bird to Heaven conveyed
And made it blossom there.

CHAPTER TWELVE

IN THE WILDERNESS

ELIZA LYNCH was indeed lonely and did not have a friend in the world unless she could count Colonel Francisco von Wisner de Morgersten.

The Baron von Wisner was an Austro-Hungarian aristocrat, who it was rumoured had had to leave Vienna under a cloud because of homosexual scandal in Court circles. He had wandered round the world as a soldier of fortune until finally he had settled in Asuncion where he was useful to Francisco Solano as a Military adviser and technician. The Hungarian cavalry officer was tall and, true to type, had aquiline features, bushy eyebrows, a hooked nose and a moustache that twirled up at the ends. Francisco did not resent his friendship with Eliza because it was a well-known fact that the Baron was not interested in ladies. He and Eliza shared the joke that they were the only two civilized people in Asuncion. Once or twice a week he would come and pay his respects to Madame Lynch and Eliza would look forward to his visits. He used her house as a haven of European culture and she confided her troubles and discussed her projects.

Eliza was never idle. She had imported the services of M. de Cluny to open an Academy of Music and to teach French. Then she had invited Luisa Balet and Dorotea Dupart to come to Asuncion and start an Academy for young ladies on the lines of a finishing school in France. It is a pity that we know so little of these two ladies. Were they old friends of Eliza's family? or were they demi-mondaines whom Eliza had befriended for old times sake and set up as school mistresses? It would be nice to think of them as ageing cocottes teaching deportment to the young ladies of Asuncion. But her immediate concern was the opening of the new theatre in Asuncion and how to get even with Madame Cochelet.

"An open cabal has been formed against me by Madame Laurent-Cochelet, the wife of the French Minister."

"My dear Eliza, why trouble yourself about her. She is nothing but a sour-faced provençal."

"She pretends to look askance at the morals of 'La Parisienne' as she calls me."

"Madame, in a few years M. Offenbach will be writing an opera about you called 'La Paraguenne'."

Eliza laughed. It was thanks to von Wisner that she kept a sense of humour.

Due to her arch-enemy Madame Laurent-Cochelet, Eliza found herself excluded from activities she had helped to foster. With a view to encouraging the arts, Eliza had prevailed upon Francisco to invite a renowned Spanish actor from Madrid, Indelfonso Bermejo to found a National theatre in Paraguay. The volatile Spaniard had arrived accompanied by his wife ironically called dona Pura and had immediately proceeded to ingratiate himself with General Lopez. Francisco, despite his antipathy towards all Spaniards, had fallen under the showman's spell and had offered him the post of superintendent of schools as well as his duties at the theatre. As soon as the Bermejos arrived in Asuncion, Madame Laurent-Cochelet had poisoned them against the Irish concubine with the consequence that Eliza's patronage was not invited nor was her advice sought in the new venture. Eliza, seething with suppressed rage, decided to bide her time and kept aloof from the entire enterprise. In one respect only was Eliza adamant; she would not permit Bermejo to import actors from Spain. "If this is a National theatre the players must be Paraguayan," she had pleaded and Francisco had seen her point of view. But she overlooked the fact that actors recruited on the spot had never set foot on any stage nor even seen a play performed. For months the town of Asuncion had only one topic of conversation—the debut of the new play written especially for the ocassion by Idelfonso Bermejo. He had chosen as a theme the Paraguayan epic La Maldonada, a Spanish woman who, at the time of the conquest was befriended by a lion cub from the warlike Guarani. The part of La Maldonada was played, in a strident, sibilant way by Senora Bermejo. Finally after months of preparation the great event took place. Hector Varela, an Argentine journalist who was present wrote the following account which appeared in the press in Buenos Aires.

"On the opening night of the new theatre, the high Society of Asuncion attended. In the box of honour, the broad faced and corpulent Dictator sat with his wife and two daughters. In the box sat General Francisco Lopez and Colonel Venancio Lopez, sons of the Dictator.

"Madame Eliza Lynch was seated in the centre box, gorgeously dressed and displaying many jewels. Even a famous courtesan like Cora Pearl, the most fashionable for a while in Paris fell short of awaking the jealous envy in the Ladies of the Faubourg St. Germain that Madame Lynch, more resplendent and enticing than I have ever seen her, awakened that night in the ladies of Asuncion.

"The Gentlemen all watched her with definitely respectful admiration. The ladies gave her hostile looks, the meaning of which was perfectly obvious.

"Lopez was really an imposing figure. One rarely sees a more impressive sight than this great tidal wave of human flesh. He is a veritable mastodon, with a pear shaped face, narrow forehead and heavy pendulous jowls.

"During the entire performance, the President ostentatiously wore an enormous hat, quite appropriate to him and equally suitable either for a museum of curiosities or for the Buenos Aires carnival.

"The performance of the players can be dismissed with a line. It was as ridiculous as Lopez's hat."

"During the evening I watched Lopez for a sign of any impression produced upon him witnessing a play for the first time in his life. It was like watching a stone in a field. He is a master in the art of concealing emotion. At the end of the tedious proceedings, without any display of either approval or disapproval, the old monarch of the jungles rose and left, ponderously followed by the soldiers of his Praetorian guard."

CHAPTER THIRTEEN

A RIVER EXCURSION

THE event was a fiasco and the Bermejos were sent back to Europe in ridicule, but the Laurent-Cochelets remained as a thorn in Eliza's side. The climax came at the inauguration of the new French colony at Nueva Burdeos in the Chaco. The five hundred emigrants that Napoleon III had promised duly arrived and were given land. To celebrate the event the old Dictator declared a national holiday and Francisco invited the members of the diplomatic corps and all high-ranking officials to a picnic luncheon that was held at the new settlement. It was arranged for the men to set out on horseback and for the ladies to follow by river steamer; Madame Laurent-Cochelet, as was only natural, was invited to be guest of honour, a proposition which she accepted without realizing that Eliza would be acting as official hostess. It was Francisco's way of obliging the women of Asuncion to be civil to Madame Lynch.

The small ship was decorated with bunting, flags and evergreens. The band played on deck and Madame Lynch resplendent in white lace stood at the top of the gangway to receive the guests. Madame Laurent-Cochelet followed by the ladies of Asuncion, both the foreign and native element tripped laughingly on board; and one and all ignored their hostess. Madame Lynch never moved a muscle.

In the brilliant sunshine the river boat got under way. The sound of lapping water caused by the swish of the revolving paddles could be heard above the animated talk. The women formed into groups and continued to behave as if they were unaware of Madame Lynch's presence. Towards midday white coated waiters produced trestle tables which they spread with

damask table cloths and gleaming silver. The guests sat themselves down to await the succulent repast. Roast turkeys,
sucking pigs, baby lambs and tricolour ice creams made their
appearance and still no one had spoken to Madame Lynch.
When Eliza went to preside at the table of honour she found
the ladies huddled so close together that there was no room
for her. Suddenly she turned round to the waiters and said in
a loud voice "Throw the food overboard."

And for ten hours the perspiring ladies, famished and
thirsty were deprived of both food and drink while Eliza kept
them weighing anchor mid stream between Asuncion and the
Chaco coast.

It was a joke after Francisco's own heart and for many a
day he and Eliza had a good laugh but Eliza's laughter was
hard and bitter. Her whole being filled with hatred and contempt for humanity. These people had twisted her soul. For
eight years she had endured their ostracism; now, her character changed. She became ruthless, calculating and hard as
granite.

A week or so after the episode on the river the Colonel
arrived to pay his customary call. "Madame, why do you stay
in Paraguay may I ask?" Von Wisner bent over and kissed
Eliza's hand.

Eliza lay back reclining on a chaise longue. She was a vision
in frills and maribou. Wearily she answered. "What can I do
with four bastards and a fifth on the way?"

The Colonel, ever Teutonically correct, was somewhat
taken aback. Only a Gentlewoman, and Irish at that, could
have retaliated with such extreme candour, he thought. "I
apologize, Madame."

"It is of no importance. I am not a maternal woman, Senor,
and I am tired of having babies."

"Nature cannot be ignored," said the Colonel primly.

"You may be quite certain it won't happen again."

"And what will you do to prevent it?"

"I will keep the General supplied with girls."

The Austro-Hungarian sat back with an amused expression

on his face. He was a man of the world. His own preference was boys but his little weakness made him the more charming and understanding.

Eliza enjoyed these afternoons. With the Colonel she felt at ease. With Francisco she had to be clever, crafty, brilliant, passionate, tender, all the things that he wanted according to his moods and above everything else an interested listener but with the Colonel she could be completely natural.

"What are they saying about me now?"

Von Wisner cleared his throat. He was a kind hearted man but he could not resist a bit of gossip. "It is whispered, dear lady, that don Francisco is getting tired of you."

"Really how interesting," she retorted, "Surely my condition belies the fact."

"I am only repeating what I heard," said the Colonel petulantly.

"And who is supposed to be my successor?"

"The daughter of Berges."

Eliza raised her eyebrows and settled herself comfortably on her cushions.

"Have you also heard that Berges came to see me?" she asked. "He wanted me to use my influence on having him named Minister of Foreign Affairs."

The Colonel blew excited little puffs with his cigar.

"I was well aware that Francisco lusted after his daughter, the one who wears roses stuck behind her ears. So I replied very diplomatically that I would speak to the General about his appointment and suggested that he brought his daughter on a visit to the Palace. I knew that that crafty old fox was only too eager to sacrifice her honour to further his ambitions. Francisco was only waiting for a chance to deflower the girl, she was only too eager to surrender and I welcomed the opportunity to allow someone else to shoulder the burden of matrimony. In that way everybody was pleased; and you can see the result for yourself. Don Jose Berges has been appointed Minister of Foreign Affairs, that full bosomed girl has temporarily become his mistress and Francisco has never been so attentive to me in his life nor showered me with more presents. He may be insatiable but I have now learnt how to manage him. As long as I live he shall never lack for mistresses and I swear that this is the last time that I shall enjoy the pleasures of motherhood."

The Colonel looked at Eliza with real admiration. "Madame, you are indeed worthy of the title "Empress of the River Plate" said the Colonel as he took his leave.

"A labourer is indeed worthy of his hire," said Eliza rather tartly.

Indeed the little Berges had only succeeded in bringing them closer together. In the succeeding months Francisco no longer felt under an obligation to conceal his little indiscretions and he took her more than ever into his confidence. She was the only person who understood him, the only person to whom he turned to. If he had loved her before now he simply worshipped her and she, for her part, felt released. Unhampered by childbearing, she was free to plan for the future and give full rein to her ambitions. She knew that no other woman would ever have the same power over him. The only rival she need fear was Paraguay, but Eliza was equally determined to exploit his love of country in such a way that, far from being a rival, Paraguay would become an ally. Together they would become the first power in South America. She looked up to see him standing by her on the balcony. At once she pretended to put her cares behind her and assumed indifference to the outside world. She would not let him see how bitterly she had been hurt. With it all she had fallen under the spell of Paraguay and had grown to love the silver river, the blood red earth and the smell of mandarins in the torrid night. She could not go back to Europe. This was where she belonged.

This evening she called for her upright piano which was carried on to the balcony by slaves and settled herself down to play Mendelssohn's Songs Without Words. She switched without a pause to Offenbach's "La Perichole" and then strummed "La Palomita", Franciso's favourite Habanera. The children played at her feet. There was Pancho, the eldest child, a tall arrogant boy of eight, Enrique, dark and delicate, then Carlos, and lastly Leopoldo the baby, a Paraguayan cherub with blue Irish eyes.

Once the children had been taken to bed, not without tantrums, by over indulgent Guarani servants in gold ear rings, she prepared an infusion of the mate leaf. She had learned to pour the boiling water into a silver gourd, take the first sip as etiquette demanded and then pass the beverage to Francisco which he imbibed through a long silver bombilla. They talked until late, dreaming and discussing plans for the future, trade agreements, extensions to the railways, monopolies, buildings, the navy, the army, all subjects dear to their hearts.

"We have now eighty thousand men under arms."

Eliza nodded.

"You have been very patient."

Eliza did not answer. She had heard the same words for eight years. But this time an outrider was heard galloping into the courtyard. Francisco got up. "Who can it be?" The man was brought into their presence.

"Don Francisco, come at once. The President is ill. He is not expected to last the night."

CHAPTER FOURTEEN

DEATH OF CARLOS ANTONIO LOPEZ

FOR three weeks the rains fell incessantly on Asuncion. The streets became rivers of mud. All clothing, bedding, mattresses, even the houses assumed the substance of sodden paper, steaming and clammy as death. In the shuttered Palace, where chamber pots and basins were placed along the passages to receive the rain drops. leaking through the roof, don Carlos lay dying of dropsy. It was a question of days, perhaps hours. He had been lingering thus for nearly a month. Barefooted messengers, with newspapers held overhead to ward off the tropical downpour, ran backwards and forwards from the Cabildo to the Presidential Palace to learn and deliver the latest bulletin. Round the bed of sickness the family prayed and cried so loudly that their wails became contagious and even the dying man began to sob.

Dona Juana held a rosary in her short dumpy fingers that were stiff with wedding rings. She wore not only her own but those of her forbears. Benigno and Venancio knelt ponderously at the end of the bed and crossed themselves repeatedly. Inocencia and Rafaela prayed holding their palms together in an attitude of supplication, not so much for the salvation of their father's immortal soul but for God's protection in the unforseeable future. Their husbands, don Saturnino Bedoya and General don Vicente Barrios, both pompous and pretentious, sat fanning themselves on upright chairs placed against the wall at the farther end of the room. The chamber was in partial darkness as a protection against the fierce heat. A huge crucifix hung on the wall behind the iron bedstead where a lank mosquito net had been pulled aside to allow the dying man to receive "Extreme Unction" from the hands of Father Palacios. The priest had a suave ingratiating manner. He whispered into the President's ear, "I assure you that you need have no fears about the hereafter. You can set your mind at rest. Have faith and rely on the goodness of the Lord. I have no doubt that Your Excellency will forego your term in purgatory and be called straight to the throne of the Almighty." He was just about to anoint the dying man's chest, his hands and his feet with the holy oils when there was a rustle of musketry and Francisco stormed into the room followed by an armed guard. The President looked as white as putty. His face was swollen and painfully distorted. Only his eyes had a glimmer of life; all he seemed to implore was to be left alone. Behind Francisco stood a notary with a sheet of parchment and a quill pen. The guard took one step forward.

"Father, it is imperative that you sign this deed."

Dona Juana screamed "Francisco, this is sacrilegious. You are in the presence of God.

The General pushed the priest to one side and held the document over his father's head. The guard advanced another step. Dona Juana sobbed. "Francisco you are torturing your father. You are committing him to hell for eternity."

Despite his mother's entreaties he placed a pen in the dying man's hand and pressed him to add a codicil to his will which read, "I, Carlos Antonio Lopez, hereby bequeath to my eldest son, the Presidency of Paraguay."

The Dictator, panting and sweating, clasped the pen with swollen fingers and wrote his name painfully and laboriously. When he reached the final letter in the alphabet his digits stiffened. The bones had to be broken to tear away the instrument with which he had signed away his country.

Francisco did not wait to console his mother but walked out of the room followed by his notary and escort. He marched straight to the Cabildo where he seized the Government papers and the keys of the Treasury. He ordered the streets to be patrolled by armed guards and he declared a state of siege. Then he convoked Congress. Town criers were despatched to summon the members. The bewildered delegates came running in twos and threes across the plaza and hurried towards the Assembly Hall.

At that moment the great bell of the Cathedral tolled announcing to the population that don Carlos Antonio Lopez, the second Dictator of Paraguay had been summoned to face his Maker. The people crept stealthily out of their houses as if seeking companionship from each other. There was a stillness in the air, breathless and oppressive. It took the gentle Gaurani some time to realize that the rain had stopped. Steam rose from the damp sodden earth and lay in the sky like a cloud. A phenomenon that made the superstitious whisper to each other, "Behold, the soul of the dead man rising to Heaven."

Francisco stood like a bull facing the Assembly. He was surounded by his own personal bodyguard who were known as aca-caraya, monkey heads, because their brass helmets were decorated with monkey tails that hung down to their waists.

In a hushed silence he made the announcement, "My august father is dead. May his spirit rest in peace." Then brandishing don Carlos's will in his hand he said in a voice that left little room for contradiction. "The late lamented Dictator has seen fit to name me his natural successor. It was his last wish that I, and I alone, should assume the Presidency of Paraguay." To give weight to his utterance he added "I need not remind you that the military strength of this country lies in my hands. I only await your constitutional assent," and he looked round defiantly as if daring any one to contradict him.

Presented with a coup d'etat, the members of the Assembly had little option and bowed to the inevitable, but wishing to preserve the semblance of democracy they got down from their seats and went into a huddle. "He is right. There is no one better suited to serve the country. Has he not travelled in Europe? Is he not indoctrinated with new ideas? Who else?"

The delegates returned to their places and the speaker don Pedro Lozcano, President of the Supreme Court got up and proclaimed, "Francisco Solano Lopez, not only do we vote you President, but we acknowledge you President for life. May Your Excellency be spared many years."

Only one voice was raised against him and that belonged to his tutor Father Maiz. "Arrest that man," thundered the new President. "Imprison him." Then in a bland voice he continued. "It would give us much pleasure to see a monument raised to the memory of my father." Immediately fifty thousand pesos were voted by the servile Assembly to erect a statue of don Carlos in the plaza.

His Excellency struck an attitude and said, "Before dismissing this assembly, I would like it known that it is our pleasure and desire that from this day onwards Madame Eliza Lynch should enjoy the same privileges as those usually accorded to the wife of a head of State. I have every confidence that my countrymen as well as the Corps Diplomatique will respect my wishes in this matter."

CHAPTER FIFTEEN

QUEEN OF PARAGUAY

MADAME LAURENT-COCHELET, the wife of the French Minister was the first to call, "A votre service, Madame."

Eliza trying to forget this woman's attitude in the past answered, "C'est notre devoir de travailler ensemble pour le bien du Paraguay." The conventions were observed but what could a woman from Clermont-Ferrand have in common with one who had been one of the brightest lights of the Second Empire.

Mrs. Washburn was the next to pay an official visit. Eliza received the wife of the American Minister politely if somewhat aloofly. Eliza presided over the tea table which they took English fashion seated on the balcony of the new pink Palace. Eliza found Mrs. Washburn a dull little woman who could only talk about mosquito nets, illnesses and the merits of New Jersey.

After Mrs. Washburn came Senhora Leite Pereira, the wife of the Portuguese Consul. She was Paraguayan by birth but had lived for some years in Lisbon which had given her a veneer of European culture. By degrees all the ladies of Asuncion came to pay their respects and not only the wives of the representatives of the Diplomatic Corps but the straight-laced members of the old Spanish nobility. Some were driven by curiosity, some hoping to advance their husbands' careers and some came under pressure from Lopez. Invariably they followed the same procedure. In the morning they sent their slaves to enquire if the Senora would be at home that day. On receiving a reply in the affirmative they would appear in the late afternoon overdressed and wearing an excess of jewels. One by one they turned up, including Lopez's sisters looking like Bavarian Easter eggs. Inocencia and Rafaela were identical except that one could have fitted inside the other. All the guests went into ectasies over the Sèvres tea cups. They raved over Eliza's gowns, spoilt the children, admired the bibelots and gorged quantities of *dulces de Leche*. Eliza wore a fixed smile, knowing they would tear her to pieces the moment that her back was turned. One and all offered their apologies for not having called sooner. Eliza failed to remark that it had taken them eight years to make the effort. If they expected to meet a scarlet woman that Francisco Solano had picked up on the trottoirs of Paris, they encountered a highly polished woman of extreme beauty who spoke English, French, Spanish and Guarani fluently and who made them feel parochial by showing up their ignorance. Eliza forced herself to be polite but she felt nothing but contempt for these parasites who had neglected her for so long and now fawned and fussed over her.

Lopez was determined not to overlook the slightest failure on the part of any one to observe Eliza's rank and gave full vent to his spleen when Senor Viana de Lima, the new Brazilian Minister, either through cussedness or ignorance neglected to pay his respects to Madame Lynch. To humiliate the Minister, Lopez refused to send more than one carriage to fetch him on his first official visit although a fleet of equipages were de rigueur to enable the diplomat to present his letter of Credence accompanied by his staff. Viana de Lima protested strongly but his remonstrances went unheeded. Finally, not to cause a diplomatic incident the Envoy was obliged to set off to the Government Palace by himself leaving his secretaries to follow in cabs.

A similar incident occurred in the case of the Hon. Edward Thornton, accredited British Minister to Asuncion. Thornton was no stranger to Lopez. The Foreign Office with conspicuous lack of tact had sent as representative a man who in former days had taken the President as hostage for the life of Constatt, a circumstance that did not endear him to Lopez, and what is more, he was now adamant in his refusal to acknowledge the "Paraguayan Pompadour" as he expressed himself in a letter to Lord John Russell.

"What do we do with this pirate?" Francisco had asked Eliza.

"He must be taught a lesson," she had answered.

Consequently he was not even sent a carriage but was subjected to the humiliation of proceeding to the Palace on foot. Lopez received him seated at his desk with his hat on and treated him in such an off hand manner that Mr. Thornton left the country immediately and wrote again to his superior at the Foreign Office, "though the Government of the elder Lopez was a despotism that of his son is indescribably worse. The new President has already developed into a tyrant so vain, arrogant and cruel that there was no misery, suffering or humiliation to which all within his power were not exposed."

That may have been the attitude of the British representative but on the other hand Lopez felt he could afford to snap his fingers at him for he had just received a letter from the Emperor of the French, Napoleon III who had been one of the first to be informed of Lopez's rise to power and had answered as follows:

General,

I have been very touched by your personal letter and its warm recollection of your visit to My Imperial court.

Believe me, I assure you, that I too remember them with pleasure. I have had occasion to appreciate your noble qualities which do you honour and therefore it is with that knowledge that I congratulate your country in electing you to safeguard her destiny.

It has filled me with great pleasure to look with admiration at the remarkable progress which Paraguay made under the rule of your illustrious father, may he rest in peace, and I have no doubt that under your wise and patriotic direction, your country will continue her progress along the path of civilization.

In expressing my cordial best wishes for your personal happiness and for the dignity of your office, it pleases me to offer you my personal esteem. In so far as I can, I pray to Almighty God to bless and preserve you.

Given by my hand in the Palace of the Tuileries
Your good friend
NAPOLEON

January 1st, 1863.

Francisco, remembering his visit to St. Cloud, which had made a lasting impression on him, decided to form a shadow court at Asuncion. Colonel von Wisner was given the post of Lord Chamberlain and two of the most distinguished young women of Asuncion, Senora Juliana Echegaray de Martinez and dona Dolores Carisimo de Jovellanos were chosen as ladies in waiting to Eliza. The former was sprightly, not unlike a little sparrow and the latter was tall and gainly. Mention must also be made of dona Isidora Diaz, the sister of General Jose Diaz who was appointed mistress of the robes. Eliza found them useful to keep her informed of the gossip around her.

Shortly after the President had helped himself to power he gave his first official dinner for the members of the Corps Diplomatique, none of whom dared refuse. The guests drove their carriages to the bottom of the ornamental steps, which arose in stately zigzags to the balustraded terrace overlooking the orange groves. They were received by the Lord Chamberlain, the members of the household and the ladies in waiting. The Baron von Wisner was dressed in the uniform of a Colonel in the Hungarian Hussars. His doublet was embroidered in silk frogs and, in spite of the heat, he wore an astrakhan collar.

The guests included the representatives of the United States, France, Brazil, Portugal and Uruguay. Colonel Thompson, an English engineer, Baron von Treunfeld, the Director of Telegraphs and Baron Clurey. There were at least six Generals present, Barrios, Resguin, Estegarribi Robles, Alen and Martinez, the husband of Eliza's dame de compagnie. Sanchez, the Vice President, a cadaverous looking man stood talking to Berges, the Minister of Foreign Affairs, a sly and lachrymose individual who had both his daughter and Madame Lynch to thank for his high position. Lopez's sisters Inocencia and Rafaela were prominent among the notabilities assembled. They wore identical dresses of black corded silk a colour that did not suit their sallow complexions. Their husbands don Saturnino Bedoya and don Vicente Barrios stood awkwardly holding glasses of spirits to their lips to give them strength to go on bullying their wives who otherwise would get the better of them. The last to arrive were the President's brothers Benigno and Venancio. They were both massive and gross but whereas Benigno was elephantine and syphilitic, Venancio was sexually underdeveloped, beardless and spoke in a high falsetto voice.

Once the guests were assembled they were herded by the members of the household towards a miniature Galerie de Glace overlooking the main courtyard where a table had been set for fifty people. Presently the double doors at the far end of the Gallery were flung open by a couple of flunkeys and Eliza and Francisco made their entrance hand in hand. That they emerged from the bedroom gave rise to a certain amount of concealed hilarity. Lopez was in evening dress and wore the Presidential band across his chest while Eliza was attired in white satin and crowned with a diadem of brilliants. It can only be regretted that there was no Winterhalter at the Court of Asuncion to do justice to Madame Lynch's starlike beauty.

Eliza and Francisco sat at the centre of the long table on either side of the bishop in his black soutane as if wishing to bask under his cloak of respectability.

The President had only recently bestowed the bishopric of Asuncion on Father Palacios after it had fallen in abeyance on the death of his uncle. The simplemindedness of the new head of the diocese had not deterred Lopez in his choice as he could now change the gospel according to his liking.

Palacios's knowledge of theology appears to have been a little shaky. Cunningham Graham tells us "that one day whilst Madame Lynch's children were playing with a Noah's ark, they could not find the figure of one of Noah's sons. His mother scolded him and told him to take more care of his toys. Bishop Palacios, who was present said "Do not scold the child, Madame, there could not have been three figures, for Noah only had two sons, and as all the world knows their names were Cain and Abel."

The new Bishop, however, was restricted in his privileges. Lopez would not allow him to use a throne nor was he permitted to have the church bells rung for him when he entered or left the Cathedral. These were the prerogatives of the President alone.

A certain consternation was caused at the end of the first state dinner party when Eliza got up from the table and none of the ladies present could find their shoes. They were obliged to walk out of the dining room barefooted and send their slaves to retrieve their slippers from a tangled heap under the banqueting table.

CHAPTER SIXTEEN

THE BALL

ON the first anniversary of Lopez's accession he was awakened by a salute of twenty-one guns. Then all day long hundreds of hands took it in turn to beat, with monotonous rhythm the Goma, an immense Indian drum which was set up on the hills behind Asuncion. Marquees were erected in the Plaza where the population could dance and imbibe free drinks of cana. There were race meetings, open air fiestas and public entertainments of all kinds including a bull fight which took place in the arena, a vast amphitheatre capable of seating several thousands. The circular building, open to the skies, was covered over with canvas not unlike a circus tent to shield the people from the fierce sun. The tiers were festooned with garlands of flowers and mantillas. The vast auditorium glittered with azure and gold, making the white *tupois* of the native women shine the dazzlingly in contrast.

When the spectators saw General Lopez and Madame Lynch, accompanied by their four children, dressed in ponchos, silver spurs and wide brimmed sombreros, take their places in the centre box which had been hung with red velvet and muslin curtains, a huge roar went up "Viva Lopez" "Caria Guazu" "Viva Madama Lavinche", a corruption of Madame Lynch, which was later shortened further to "Lavinche", a name which stuck to her for good.

Only the bulls seemed to lack animation and had to be prodded to put up a good fight. Every time a toro was killed, the carcase was dragged by a funeral hearse and presented as an offering to Madama Lavinche who graciously acknowledged the tribute and threw carnations at the Matador.

Reminiscent of some great Roman carnival, there were, besides bull fights, races and music, games—the favourite of which was "La Sortija" in which a rider had to gallop at full speed towards a golden hoop and pierce it with his sword. Between the various items the ring was filled with masqueraders, masked and hooded figures called "Cambas Rangas" who pretended to be tumblers but in reality were spies placed there by Police to mingle with the crowd to gauge public opinion as regards the Government of Lopez.

On the 7th of November, Francisco Solano and Madame Lynch were present at a ball given in their honour by the Foreign Colony of Asuncion at the Club Nacional. They set out in an open landau escorted by outriders carrying lighted torches and drove under triumphal arches that had been erected along the principal street of Asuncion as far as the entrance to the club.

On their arrival, they were met by members of the Patrician families such as Juan Francisco Decond and Carlos and Jesuando Saguier as well as representatives of the diplomatic corps and the principal foreign residents including Doctor Stewart, a British subject, personal physician to Lopez. He was a dapper little man with twinkling eyes who had served in the Crimean war. The hall was decorated with palm trees and garlanded with evergreens and "Camelotes" water lilies that grew in the neighbouring lagoons. Washburn, the American Minister in Asuncion, was present and recalled the scene.

"This ball, like most balls in Asuncion, was strictly an official affair. People were invited to attend, but the invitation among the natives was equivalent to a command. The imported favourite (Madame Lynch) was the leader of fashion and had the almost unlimited directions of all such matters; at this ball she prescribed the dress for all, assigning the garb of Swiss Shepherdess for one, an Italian fruit seller for another, and prescribing for each some peculiar style of costume but arraying herself in the gorgeous style of Queen Elizabeth."

Eliza's dress was made of cloth of gold. Wide paniers hung on each side; the long bodice was completely sewn with seed pearls. Her face stood out in relief before a fan shaped ruffle and her golden hair was elaborately dressed with diamonds and pearls. She had copied Holbein's portrait of Queen Elizabeth Tudor. Despite her beauty there was a disquiet about her presence which made Dr. Stewart write to his brother in Edinburgh. "Nobody felt at ease in her presence." The ball was opened by Francisco and Eliza who danced "El Cielo," a complicated measure, half minuet, half waltz. Lopez was in full dress uniform and wore the order of merit. He danced well in spite of the fact that he was beginning to put on weight. Whereas in his younger days he had looked like the Prince of Wales, now at the age of thirty seven, he resembled Napoleon III with a touch of the tarbrush.

As the General and his consort moved ceremoniously through the complicated figures, the spectators joined in the chorus. From the furthermost corner of the ball-room, from the gallery above and the benches below they burst into song.

Ay cielo. Ay cielo.
Este cruel amor . . .

All eyes were on Eliza, who brought both romance and a touch of history to Asuncion. When the dance was over, Lopez went and sat on a throne at the far end of the ballroom, under a red velvet canopy embroidered with the Paraguayan coat of arms. Washburn says it was the first time that Lopez had indicated his intentions of having himself crowned King. Eliza sat on a stool by his side while his two sisters, dressed as Dresden Shepherdesses stood immediately behind him. Everybody was expected to pay their respects to the President beginning with the Corps Diplomatique. When it came to Mr. Washburn's turn to greet the President, he lifted his glass and said, "I drink to the health of the illustrious President of Paraguay. Let his reign be as honourable to himself and as advantageous to his country as was that of his distinguished predecessor and father." Instead of replying Lopez looked straight through him. The American Minister could not understand what he had done to deserve Lopez's displeasure until a few day's later he received an official letter complaining that he had not been in fancy dress.

The quadrille that followed was danced diagonally across the ballroom so that the dancers should at no moment turn their backs on Lopez.

But even as the General sat enthroned beside his mistress he was planning to betray her. Unbeknown to Eliza he had written to the Emperor of Brazil Pedro II offering his hand in marriage to the Infanta, no doubt thinking that a Princess of Royal blood would be more useful to him for dynastic reasons than a left-handed consort. Self-pityingly he comforted himself with the thought that even Napoleon had had to sacrifice his Josephine.

CHAPTER SEVENTEEN

DECLARATION OF WAR

In Rio de Janeiro, Lopez's letter was received with the utmost scorn. The Prime Minister was heard to say to his Majesty. "The pretensions of this upstart to aspire the hand of a Braganza!" The Emperor, who by inclination was more of a scientist than a monarch, merely smiled and thought it prudent to ignore the letter. After a wait of months Lopez pressed for an answer. On the strength of his second effort he got a reply to the effect that the Infanta was as yet too young to contemplate matrimony. But when, a short time after she became engaged to her cousin the Comte d'Eu, an Orleans Prince, Francisco Solano was mortally offended and took it as a personal slight. From then on he was determined to pick a quarrel with Brazil and make her pay for the insult. Unknowingly, the Emperor of Brazil had done a great service to Madame Lynch. From that day onwards, Lopez, like any other contrite husband, tried to make amends and wrote to the Pope asking for a special dispensation to enable him to marry Madame Lynch on the grounds that her first marriage had not been consummated. Above all he wanted Panchito his eldest son to be declared legitimate and recognised as the natural successor of the Lopez dynasty. The children took the name of Lopez instead of the surname Lynch.

The chance to play his hand against Brazil took place sooner than he expected. On the 14th of October, 1864 Brazil invaded Uruguay on the pretext of suppressing a revolution. For years Uruguay had been in the throes of a civil war. There were two parties continually struggling for power, the Blancos and the Colorados. Both sides consisted of scattered groups of gauchos who rode through the Pampas at random sweeping down on some isolated community and conscripting the males at the point of a bayonet. Any resistance was met with a quick thrust of a knife across the throat, a prank that was commonly called playing the violin.

While Brazil sided with the rebels under the leadership of General Flores, the established government appealed to Lopez for help and sent don Antonio de la Carrera, one time Minister to London, as special envoy to Asuncion to conclude a military alliance with Paraguay. Lopez would not commit himself but sent a formal protest to Viana de Lima, the Brazilian Minister in Asuncion in which he said, "I regard any occupation of Uruguayan territory by the Brazilians as infringing the equilibrium of the States of Rio de la Plata which concerns the Republic of Paraguay as a guarantor of its security, peace and prosperity and I protest against such an act in the most solemn manner and disclaim from the present time all responsibility for any ulterior consequences that may arise from the present declaration".

Lopez sent a copy of the manifesto to the head of the Argentine Republic but his attempts at arbitration were ridiculed in the press. He was told not to interfere in matters concerning countries far better civilized than Paraguay. The same article referred to him as an Indian Chief, to Asuncion as a collection of wigwams and to Madame Lynch as an Indian squaw.

This was too much for the niece of an officer who had fought with Nelson at Trafalgar. "Show them who is the master in South America. We must avenge the insult." Eliza stormed. "Now is the time to attack Brazil while she is occupied in raping her neighbour. She cannot conduct a war on two fronts. We will gain a great victory and you can dictate your own terms. This is your chance to show your strength. We can become the most powerful country in South America."

Lopez did not need any encouragement but was awaiting the best moment to strike when he would be confident that he would emerge victorious from the conflict. Making a pretence of acting constitutionally, he convoked congress and extracted twenty five million dollars for ships and armaments. On the strength of that he sent don Candido Bareiro to Europe as diplomatic representative. Don Candido was a shrewd business man with black beady eyes and a greying beard. He was given instructions to buy sixty thousand rifles in France, one hundred thousand cases of cartridges, forty-two cases of bayonets as well as uniforms and equipment of every description for a modern army. As an after-thought he was ordered to buy the latest machine guns in Prussia. Lopez was hesitant in beginning a war until he had in his possession all the armaments on order, knowing full well that once hostilities started he would be cut off from the outside world.

At the same time he appointed don Felix Egusquiza to be his confidential agent and commercial attaché in Buenos Aires to make more easy the import of armaments from Europe that had to come by way of the Argentine. At one moment Egusquiza is instructed to buy a new landau and yards of muslin for Madame Lynch: at the next he is ordered to negotiate the sale of yerba mate to Valparaiso and Mendoza: yet again he is told to expect a consignment of armaments from England. In a letter to his agent written on August 21st, 1863, Lopez expresses himself satisfied that "the rifles and carbines brought on the *Una* from Liverpool have arrived safely".

On September 6th he is writing again. "I am sorry that the 'Paragueri' was unable to bring the long awaited cargo. I am hoping that by now you will have received a further consignment. If such is the case Lieutenant Herreros has been ordered to do everything he can to expedite the transhipment of these articles either at Beunos Aires or Montevideo. It is essential that we gain time in case a blockade is enforced which of course depends on the outcome of the present situation which is critical. Should such an emergency arise I am counting on you to do all you can to establish lines of communication with us either by hand or by sea and keep us supplied with material."

On the 28th of the same month he is writing again. "Send two thousand pounds to Mr. Robert Stewart to purchase railway lines and despatch as soon as possible."

Early in October he again puts pen to paper. A note of urgency has crept into his letters. "I am expecting a cargo of rifles by the ship that left Liverpool on August 8th. If these do not arrive in time to catch the "Paragueri" they will have to come on the "Igurey". Failing both, commandeer a ship expressly for that purpose."

In the spring Lopez decided to hold manoeuvres and departed for Cerro Leon, a large military camp, leaving Madame Lynch in Asuncion. He drilled his troops so hard, according to Colonel Thompson, that many of them died of overtraining. In case an emergency should arise he dispersed his troops strategically. He stationed seventeen thousand men at Encarnacion, ten thousand at Humaita, seven thousand at Asuncion, not to mention scattered troops in the forts of Curupaity and Paso Pucu. The remainder, amounting to thirty thousand he left at Cerro Leon. It was a formidable army and one that could well realize the ambitions of Simon Bolivar. Still he hesitated.

CHAPTER EIGHTEEN

THE MARQUES DE OLINDA

At three o'clock on the morning of November 9th, 1864, Senor Vasquez Sagastume Uruguayan Minister at Asuncion demanded an audience of Madame Lynch. There was but a solitary sentinel on duty. He clicked his heels and called "Cabo de Guardia." A Corporal appeared from the Guard House. "What is the nature of your business at this hour of the night, Senor?" The Guard was told it was a matter of life and death.

Don Vasquez Sagastume was a polished diplomat with a veneer of culture who liked to air his English. In the past he had never missed an opportunity to flatter Lopez and sent costly gifts to the favourite.

After some time the heavy doors were unbolted and he was admitted into the Palace. The guard took him up a spiral staircase which led to the private oratory where Eliza received him thinking that the sanctuary of a chapel would protect her from the accusations of Lopez's spies, who before the night was over would inform the General that she had received a man alone. "Ma'am," said the Uruguayan Minister, "I have just been advised by a certain Juan Soto, formerly a merchant of Asuncion, that a Brazilian steamer the Marques de Olinda, carrying Senor Carneiro Campos, the new Governor of Mato Grosso, as well as a large quantity of cargo and armaments, is on her way to Corumba. I do not have to tell you Ma'am, that the Brazilians are in the ignominious position of having to sail through Paraguayan waters to get to their own province of Mato Grosso. I have come to implore you to take action and seize the Brazilian steamer."

Eliza saw at once the possibilities that such a move would

open up. Madame Lynch had had an anxious year. Lopez was not the only one to employ spies. Eliza had her own secret service who had kept her informed of Lopez's overtures to Brazil. Hurt and resentful, she had decided that the wisest course was to pretend complete ignorance of the network of intrigue behind her back. Now she knew that her silence had paid dividends and that Lopez had learnt his lesson. Her position was assured; perhaps it was even stronger than it had ever been. He needed her as much as she needed him. Together they would be invincible. She had no doubt that Francisco would marry her just as soon as they could annul her marriage with M. Quatrefages. They had asked the Pope for a dispensation but it was a complicated situation. She had married a Roman Catholic in the Church of England which meant that it was binding contract in her case although not valid in the case of her husband. No doubt the situation would resolve itself in time. With a complete lack of logic she wanted war with Brazil to punish them for having slighted Francisco yet knowing that if matters had gone otherwise she would have been the first to be sacrificed. Her ambitions drove her on. She would not rest until she had seen Lopez the Napoleon of South America and herself standing by his side.

Eliza insisted that Vasquez Sagastume should depart at once for Lopez's headquarters to relay the information that he had just confided in her and supplied him with a change of mount. Don Vasquez reached the camp late on the following day.

Lopez received him in his tent which was handsomely furnished with a bed, Indian rugs and braceros. Braziers of charcoal were lighted against the strong winds that swept down from the Cordillera. Don Vasquez was not slow in coming to the point. "Once you are in possession of the "Marques de Olinda" you can dictate your own terms Sir. Be firm. Show that you have the upper hand. The status quo of South America is in your hands."

The General no longer hesitated. He slapped Vasquez Sagastume on the back and said "If we don't have a war with

Brazil now we shall have one at a less convenient time." An aide de camp was sent post haste to Asuncion by express engine, the first locomotive to run along the recently completed railway line, with orders for the Tacuari, the fastest vessel in his possession to capture the Marquez de Olinda. The Tacuari had no difficulty in seizing the unarmed ship and bringing her into port. The Governor of Mato Grosso was thrown into prison and the crew and the passengers were interned. On the same day, November 9th, don Jose Berges, the Minister for Foreign Affairs sent a note to Senor Viana de Lima in which he stated that "In view of the Brazilian invasion of the Banda Oriental all relations with Brazil will cease."

Washburn was flabbergasted when he heard the news and set out at once for Cerro Leon to try and remonstrate with Lopez. The United States Minister was a heavily built man who looked slightly absurd riding a small Paraguayan pony. He may have been well meaning but he was certainly no diplomat, "Why did you not wait and declare war as an ally of Uruguay instead of committing an act of piracy?", he demanded without any tact on coming fact to face with Lopez. Whereupon the President lost his temper with Washburn and shouted, "The situation of Paraguay is such that only by a war can the attention and respect of the world be secured to her. Isolated as she is, and scarcely known beyond the South American States, so she will remain until by her feats of arms she will compel other nations to treat her with more consideration."

The Dictator of Paraguay was still smarting under the insult he had received at the hands of the Brazilian Royal family.

He was determined to do something spectacular that would make his name a household word in South America. Without further ado he decided to invade the Brazilian province of Mato Grosso. This territory was almost isolated from the rest of Brazil and easier to reach by the river Paraguay than by land.

On the 14th of December, 1864, amidst general rejoicing and salvoes, three thousand men under the command of General Barrios, the President's brother-in-law, set sail for Corumba in five steamers and three schooners. The troops included two field batteries and the 6th and 7th Battalions of Mulatoes, crack regiments that went by the name of "small ears." During the embarkation General Lopez appeared in person on the landing stage to take leave of the expeditionary force and he issued a manifesto which ended up with the following words, "Soldiers! My endeavours to keep the peace have been fruitless. The Empire of Brazil, not knowing our valour and enthusiasm, provokes us to war, which challenge we are bound by our honour and dignity to accept in protection of our dearest rights."

The Paraguayan forces, reinforced by a contingent of cavalry under Resquin, a hatchet-faced General, succeeded in destroying the all-but defenceless forts of Coimbra, Albuquerque, Doradas and Miranda along the upper Paraguay. The forts had been designed as a defence against the wild Indians and consequently all the guns pointed towards the Chaco and could not be turned round. Because of the great distances the news of the capture of the Marques de Olinda had not reached the province and the Brazilians were taken completely by surprise. Corumba, the capital of Mato Grosso, fell without a shot, the province was quickly over-run and a great deal of booty fell into Paraguayan hands.

The two sons of the Baron de Villa Maria, the richest land owner in the district, who owned eighty thousand head of cattle and countless slaves, were killed but the father managed to escape with a jar full of diamonds. It took him a month to reach Rio de Janeiro on foot, guided by the stars. He was the first to inform the Emperor that his Majesty had lost his greatest province, Mato Grosso.

Lopez was intoxicated by his success, Eliza Lynch was radiant and there was general jubilation in Asuncion. Bands played all day. Flags waved from every house top and the people danced in the streets. The Buenos Aires press scathingly referred to this demonstration as St. Vitus's dance. The General held a military review at the Campo Grande, the vast plain above Asuncion, where he appeared on horseback accompanied by his sons dressed as cadets. For four hours Francisco and Eliza stood under a ramada watching the troops march past in a cloud of dust. It was estimated that more than twelve thousand men were assembled. Six regiments of artillery, four squadrons of cavalry and ten battalions of infantry armed with lock muskets, percussion guns, lances and machetes, filed by. A fully equipped medical corps brought up the rear. The soldiers were all dressed alike in white trousers and scarlet tunics. The hat or cap was the distinguishing feature. The infantry wore caps not unlike those of the French Imperial guard while the cavalry and artillery carried black leather morions. Except for the mounted regiments all the troops went barefoot. Even the better class Paraguayans who were accustomed to wearing shoes had to discard their footware on joining the ranks.

Once the parade was over a short ceremony took place. Madame Lynch received a patent of nobility, looted from the house of the Baron de Villa Maria and Lopez was presented with a trophy of Brazilian ears that had been strung together like a necklace and hung ceremonially around his neck.

CHAPTER NINETEEN

CAMPAIGN OF CORRIENTES

THE General was determined to carry the war to a successful conclusion and there and then decided to send the troops he had just reviewed to occupy the Brazilian territory of Rio do Sul. He gave the command to General Antonio Estigarribia, who was popular but more of a ladies man than a soldier.

At first all went well. Morale was high and food was plentiful. Cattle were commandeered to supply the army but nobody took into account that the Paraguayans were not a meat eating people and consequently dysentery broke out in the ranks.

Estigarribia crossed the river Parana and asked permission of the Argentine Government to proceed into Brazil through the province of Corrientes, a request that was refused on the grounds that Buenos Aires was not at war with Brazil. Lopez decided it was too late to retreat without losing face and ordered the occupation of Corrientes, which fell without resistance, on Good Friday, 1865, and two little steamers, the "25 de mayo" and the "Gualeguay" fell into his hands without firing a shot.

Lopez acted in a high handed manner because he was counting on the support of General Urquiza who had openly and repeatedly expressed his views on the policy of Mitre and had assured Lopez, through his representative, don Julio Victorica, a plausible individual with the gift of the gab, that if it came to a showdown he would side with Paraguay. His views were so universally known that Washburn, the American Minister wrote to Washington. "It is generally believed here that in any controversy with Brazil, President Lopez

D

could count with the help of General Urquiza who is as powerful in the province of Entre Rios as Lopez is in Paraguay."

Lopez convoked Congress and declared war on the Argentine on the 18th March, 1865, an act that was gazetted in the Semanario on the following day but was not received in the Argentine until thirty five days later by which time Paraguay had invaded the province of Missiones. When the news finally reached the Argentine that their country had been invaded without warning they were stunned. He was accused of treachery and of acting beyond the laws of nations and they swore not to lay down their arms until they had settled the score.

Lopez refuted the charges set by maintaining that he had sent the Argentine an intimation of hostilities on March 19th couched in the following terms:

"We hereby declare war on the Argentine until such time as our honour is satisfied in accordance with the dignity of the Paraguayan nation and her Government— Hall of Assembly; Asuncion
(signed) Jose falcon
Vice President in
fulfilment of his duties at the august National Congress.
Bernardo Ortellado
Deputy Secretary
y
Gregoria Molinas
Asuncion March 1865.

To be made public
Lopez
(countersigned)
Jose Berges
Minister of Foreign Affairs."

In replying to the Argentine's note of protest Lopez asserted that it was not his fault if the news had been withheld from the public. He could prove that he had sent a certain Lieutenant Cipriano Ayala with despatches containing the declaration of war twelve days before the occupation of Corrientes. His messenger had passed through Humaita on April 3rd and had been at Parana on the 6th and had subsequently arrived in Buenos Aires a week later, where instead of being treated with chivalry and sent back under a flag of truce he had been thrown into a common jail.

The truth of the matter was that Lopez had ordered the messenger to delay the delivery of his intimation to the parties concerned as long as possible to enable the Esmeralda, a ship he had chartered, to arrive at Asuncion with a valuable cargo of armaments and also to give Egusquiza, who had been privately informed of his intentions, time to withdraw all Paraguayan gold reserves invested in the Argentine.

The occupation of Corrientes, however, proved a disastrous move for Paraguay. Not only did it bring the Argentine into the war against her but had the effect of uniting all parties in Uruguay under General Flores, who immediately sued for a separate peace with Brazil and became their ally. Even General Urquiza, on whom Lopez had relied, held aloof. Thus Lopez and Madame Lynch, who had set out to maintain the status quo of the River Plate, found themselves at war not only with the country they had tried to befriend, but fighting the combined forces of two Presidents and one Emperor.

"March on Buenos Aires", pleaded Eliza with tears of rage in her eyes. "Abandon the campaign to Rio Grande do Sul. It can serve no purpose. The Argentine is unprepared for war. Deceitful mongrels that they are. This is the moment to bring those cut-throats to their knees. You would have no opposition, Francisco, they would welcome you as liberator." Eliza still smarted under the insults hurled at her in the press of Buenos Aires.

Francisco was sorely tempted but thought it more prudent to proceed along the lines he had originally devised. "No. No. I need an outlet to the sea. Once we have settled the score with Brazil it will be time enough to turn our attentions to the

Argentine." Instead of listening to Eliza's advice he sent General Robles to reinforce the main army and deliver the coup-de-grace.

The Paraguayans met little resistance in their advance through Missiones. At Sao Borja, Estigarribia crossed the river Uruguay with the bulk of the army leaving Duarte, his second in command, to proceed along the right bank with a vanguard of two thousand men. They advanced in parallel columns, opposite to one another and keeping in touch by canoe. Inevitably, the further they penetrated into enemy territory, the more vulnerable they became.

In August of the same year, four months after the start of the campaign, Estigarribia took the Brazilian town of Uruguayana opposite Yatai which was simultaneously occupied by Duarte. Suddenly Duarte found himself surprised by a combined force of Uruguayans and Brazilians and the two thousand men under his command were reduced to three hundred. He sent a desperate message to Robles, alleging that the Brazilians gave no quarter and beseeching him to come to his aid, not knowing that Robles had been ambushed and lost his entire force. Unfortunately this letter was intercepted by the Allies, and only led to further bitterness.

On laying down his arms Wesceslau Robles was honourably treated and received overtures from Bartlomeo Mitre suggesting that he organize an army of liberation and rescue Paraguay from the tyranny of Lopez. Since the time of the elder Lopez there were many prominent Paraguayan families living in exile in Buenos Aires and the Banda Oriental, who welcomed such a step and declared that they would willingly place themselves at his command. Furthermore Robles was assured by Mitre that he would receive the valuable help of General Urquiza. Throughout the war the Governor of Entre Rios kept promising aid first to one side and then to another and in the end did nothing but amass a huge fortune for himself. Robles was in a quandry. He did not know where his duty lay. He was torn between love of country and loyalty to Lopez. When news of his vacillation reached Lopez through

his elaborate spy system he immediately sent General Resquin, with a small force to kidnap the wavering General.
They succeeded in their objective of removing Robles from
the very jaws of the enemy and he was taken back to Humaita
in chains; after lingering for some months in prison he was
eventually shot as a traitor.

Estigarribia, meanwhile, endeavoured to retreat across the
Uruguay and found the river blockaded by four armed gunboats under the Brazilian Admiral Tamandare. At this
moment the Emperor of Brazil accompanied by his son-in-law
the Comte d'Eu arrived with a force that brought the total
Allied strength up to thirty thousand men. The Allies issued
a joint communique urging Estigarribia to surrender. To
which the Paraguayan General replied in his best South
American rhetoric,

"*Viva La Republica de Paraguay*. Your Excellencies, the
sacred ensign of liberty will not be besmirched by me.
Perish the thought. Although my bones and those of my
heroic legionnaires should find their only sepulchre among
the ruins of Uruguayana, our spirits free and proud shall
soar aloft. God preserve Your Excellencies many years.

Antonio Estigarribia."

In response to a further summons to lay down their arms
Estigarribia spoke of glory and liberty. "I answer to your
Excellencies when you enumerate to me the number of your
forces and the amount of your artillery, so much the better,
the smoke of the cannon shall be our shade. God preserve
your Excellencies many years."

After giving the Paraguayan General a few more days in
which to make up his mind the Allied Commanders called
on him for yet a third time to give himself up.

Having exhausted his ammunition as well as his adjectives
and eaten his last horse, Estigarribia surrendered. The rank
and file were taken prisoner and the officers allowed to reside
wherever they chose outside Paraguay. Estigarribia himself
was sent to Buenos Aires where he was treated with the utmost
kindness and shown great hospitality.

CHAPTER TWENTY

THE MARSHAL-PRESIDENT

ASUNCION anxiously awaited news. Hopes of a great victory ran high. If one province had fallen there was no reason to suppose why a second one should not follow suit. Estigarribia was known to have encountered little opposition. It was just a question of time.

Lopez and Eliza had taken their abode at the old Palace of Asuncion to be nearer their people in time of war. Work still went on spasmodically in the colossal mansion they had planned for themselves but the new dwelling would not be ready for many years. In the meantime they made do with the official residence in the Calle Independencia which was little changed since Francia's day. There were damp patches on the walls and the floor boards creaked.

They sat in a glass enclosed corridor that overlooked an inner patio, poring over a map and trying to trace such names as Uruguayana and San Borja. Francisco was in an expansive mood. "The Allies are at loggerheads. The Brazilians have no difficulty in raising troops by means of slavery but the Argentine Gaucho and the Uruguayo, although fearless and reckless, are undisciplined and apt to desert en masse or raid each other. I have been told on good authority that they have to be chained in gangs to be dragged to the front," he asserted. Through the thick walls they could hear the tread of men and women walking the streets in voluntary processions. The people were encouraged to make speeches and extol the virtues of the President. "He is the defender of the race, the father of our family. Mita Moroti. Our great white child" were words that drifted from without and sounded like music in Lopez's ear.

In expectation of the great victory, Eliza had organized a
ball at the club in Asuncion. Women were commanded to
wear their most elaborate gowns and to array themselves in
their finest jewels. The wary maintained that it was
"Madama's way" of estimating the value of their jewels. The
ballroom was decorated with the flags of all nations. At the
last minute the Brazilian, the Argentine and the Uruguayan
emblems had to be removed, having been hung up by mistake.
Soldiers of the garrison and men on special leave stood about
in groups eyeing the girls who arrived in the company of their
mothers. The orchestra began to tune their instruments striking those discordant sounds more exciting than any
symphony. The atmosphere was tense. Those who attended
the dance awaited breathlessly the arrival of the Presidential
party. Perhaps a great victory would be announced tonight
they thought.

The General and Madame Lynch were on the point of
setting out for the ball when an outrider came galloping up
to the Palace. He jumped off his horse and landed on the
ground at Lopez's feet. The courier handed his Excellency
a note. Lopez read the brief and turned purple. "Blasphemy!
Death! and Destruction!" Eliza thought he was about to have
a stroke. "Estigarribia has surrendered," he hissed. "This is
infamous. He shall pay for it one day. I won't rest until I see
him quartered before my eyes. There is nothing but
Treachery. Treachery all around me."

Lopez, shaking with impotent rage, shut himself up in his
room and refused to see a living soul.

Madame Lynch ordered her carriage and set off for the
dance by herself. She was determined that the defeat should
not be revealed until the following day. On her arrival she
told the welcoming committee "The President is too busy
with affairs of state to attend the dance." To render homage
to his person, however, an oil painting of the General was
placed on the empty throne to which the women genuflected
and the men were obliged to bow. Schottisches, gavottes,
waltzes and mazurkas were performed as well as the national

dances. At one moment the orchestra played with Spanish abandon, at the next they executed sad Indian melodies.

In a corner of the ballroom Eliza came across Senora Jovellanos, her lady in waiting, in floods of tears. "Que sucede?" "What is wrong?"

"I have just received the news that my husband has been killed on the battle front."

Eliza looked at her coldly. "You should rejoice. It is a privilege to die for one's country." The mistress of Solano Lopez was unmoved.

At midnight consternation was caused by the arrival of the Peinetes de Oro, the ladies of easy virtue, who demanded admittance to the ball. "What shall we do?" wailed little Senora Martinez. "Let them in," said Eliza Lynch. "This is a patriotic gathering. All classes should mingle." A beau geste that made the more aristocratic members of the community murmur behind their fans, "Madame Lavinche is only defending her own".

For three days Lopez remained in his room. His moods alternated between abject despair and uncontrollable wrath. Nobody dared go near him. Not even Panchito his eldest son, whom he adored. Eliza was the one exception. "How could Estigarribia have dared to surrender?" "Surely death is better than dishonour." "The coward. The traitor. The bastard son of a bitch," he ranted. Francisco refused to admit even to himself that any Paraguayan would stoop so low as to lay down his arms. "It is inconceivable. Bribery is the only possible explanation."

The next day a long article appeared in the Semanario, the Government owned newspaper, saying that Estigarribia had sold himself to the Argentines for ten thousand pesos. The revelation caused a demonstration to be staged in Asuncion at which Estigarribia was denounced as any enemy of Paraguay and his effigy was burnt at the stake.

On the third day Lopez emerged from his seclusion and convoked Congress. Francisco Solano appeared in full military uniform and proclaimed himself a Field Marshal. He would have liked to adopt the title of Emperor but was afraid of ridicule in the foreign press. The new rank suited him well enough for the time being.

The Marshal President then proceeded to demand that the entire nation should place their lives and their property in his hands. This was approved unanimously by a cringing Congress. At the same time, the servile members voted the Dictator a salary of sixty thousand dollars a year, a sum ten times in excess of any that his father had ever received; and to ingratiate themselves the further, the Delegates allotted another thirty thousand for the purchase in Europe of a Marshal's baton, a gold hilted sword and a wreath of oak leaves similar to Napoleon's crown intended, as the spokesman said, "for a heroic brow" and lastly to show their appreciation of Madame Lynch, the Marshal's worthy consort, they included in the order that went to Paris by way of Bolivia and Chile a coronet of brilliants studded with pear shaped pearls reminiscent of the Empress Josephine's crown.

His Excellency barely acknowledged these sops. He hunched his thick shoulders and thumping himself several times on the chest he said;

"Citizens—

The course of the war no longer allows me to continue the self sacrifice of absenting myself from the theatre of operations. I feel the necessity of personally participating in the fatigues of the brave and loyal defenders of our fatherland, thus leaving the public administration duly provided for. I depart for the seat of war to assume the duties of General in Chief of the Armies of Paraguay".

Madame Lynch was named Regent of Paraguay.

CHAPTER TWENTY-ONE

THE BATTLE OF THE RIACHUELO

On June 8th, 1865, the Marshal President left for Head-quarters in secret. The reason being that he was afraid that spies might inform the enemy of his movements. Only Eliza Lynch was on the landing stage to bid him farewell. They embraced in silence. She had come a long way since she had met him on the platform of the Gare St. Lazare. As Lopez got into the dinghy that was to row him out to the Tacuari, H.M.S. Dotteral, lying at anchor in Asuncion, manned her yards and the men, formed along the bulwarks, saluted. Lopez did not know whether to be pleased or angry that he had been recognized. The Tacuari sailed for Humaita at midnight escorted by four armed transports loaded with troops.

The first order of the General in Chief on reaching head-quarters on the following day was to recall the remaining troops that were still in occupation of Corrientes. The hurried exodus was conducted in full view of the Brazilian ironclads which made no effort to hinder them. This inertia and lack of enterprise was characteristic of the Brazilians. If the forces of Pedro II had followed up their victory over Estigarribia they could have won the war in a question of weeks. Instead, they gave Lopez time to reorganize his army and to strengthen his two most formidable strongholds, the forts of Curupaity and Humaita, each at a bend of the river Paraguay protecting the approach to Asuncion. The defences of Humaita were entrusted to Colonel Thompson, the English engineer. He ordered a triple line of earth works and a labyrinth of trenches to be built. By the time that Thompson had finished work on the fortification it was a well-nigh impregnable fort-ress mounting three hundred and eight guns.

The Brazilians dared not venture up the river, across which Lopez had placed a boom, but contented themselves with bombarding Humaita, which was perched on a cliff, from a distance. Lopez, who had promised Madame Lynch to take special precautions for his personal safety had a bomb-proof shelter erected from which he could watch the Brazilian iron-clads through a telescope. On one occasion a single cannon ball exploded so near the shelter, killing thirteen men, that Lopez was convinced that it had been aimed straight at him. He was beside himself with rage and ordered Captain Meza to destroy the Brazilian navy.

This was a daring move amounting to sheer folly because the Brazilian fleet consisted of nine ironclads while the Paraguayan had barely eight wooden ships, none of them larger than six hundred tons.

In the tropical haze of an early dawn, the little fleet steamed down the river, towing the chatas, flat bottomed rafts, that carried the troops. Meza who was a feeble old man, became so demoralized with the noise of gunfire that Mr. Watts, an Englishman and Chief Engineer of the Tacuari, was obliged to take command. He ordered the ships to file past the Brazilian fleet without firing a shot. It was not until he reached Bella Vista, a point down the river, that he issued the word of command to turn about. By this manoeuvre the Brazilians found themselves caught by the Paraguayans and unable to escape. When the top deck of the Tacuari was on a level with the bulwark of the Brazilian ship *Paranakya,* a Sergeant and a dozen men, nimble as the monkeys they despised, leapt aboard with the accuracy of acrobats and swung from one masthead to another. The Brazilians set up a howl and ran below decks. The vessel could well have been captured by the Parguayans had they secured the hatches, but the Marines, drunk with success and spirits, marched up and down the deck beating a drum. The sound seemed to stir some atavistic impulse in the minds of the Negroid Brazilian sailors because they rushed up the hatchways and charged the invaders. Like mischievous children the Paraguayans promptly jumped overboard and swam ashore laughing. The elated Brazilians now took advantage of the situation ramming the lighter vessels of the Paraguayans. The Tacuari and the Igurey contrived to escape towing the Ypora between them. Another three ships limped home in a half-sinking state. The Marques de Olinda fell on her side and drifted downstream with the current and was finally grounded off the Chaco coast. The Salto Oriental sank immediately but at a point where the river was so silted up that her hulk remained above the water line. The Brazilians sent boats to the disabled ships to take off the wounded but with their usual lethargy, made no effort to follow up the victory.

At headquarters, the General staff awaited events with the greatest anxiety. Early in the afternoon a boat came up the river bringing the tidings that the Brazilians had been routed. Lopez was beside himself with joy and telegraphed the news to Madame Lynch in Asuncion. But the hours passed and there was still no confirmation of victory.

It was not till the following morning when the maimed ships straggled in after the battle of the Riachuelo that it was learnt that instead of a success there had been disaster. Captain Meza, the officer in command of the expedition arrived at Humaita in a dying state, having been severely wounded by a musket ball that had penetrated his right lung. Lopez sent him word that if he did not die soon he would have him shot for incompetency. The Marshal was in one of his blackest moods. He ranted and raved. "The Officers are as irresponsible as the men. There is no one on whom I can rely."

At a besa mano, a levée, held that same morning at Lopez's headquarters, the Bishop made the customary panegyric instead of the Minister of War who was in disgrace. Lopez heard him through till the end with growing impatience and then he shouted "I am working for my country, for the good and honour of you all, and none help me. I stand alone. I have confidence in none of you. I cannot trust one amongst you," and then striding forwards and raising his clenched hand he cried "Cuidado. Take care. Hitherto I have pardoned offences, taken pleasure in pardoning, but now from this day on, I pardon no one".

George Frederick Masterman, a young English apothecary who was present at the levée, says in his book "Seven eventful years in Paraguay", "As I looked round on the wide circle of Officers bowing as he left the room, I saw many a blanched face amongst them for they knew that he would keep his word".

CHAPTER TWENTY-TWO

REGENT OF PARAGUAY

Eliza Lynch sat in the glass enclosed corridor of the Palace watching her children playing at soldiers in the patio. In physiognomy they were a blend of Guarani and Celt. Pancho, her first born, was the most handsome but Leopoldo was the most endearing. "Down with the Macacos" they shouted, pretending to shoot in mock warfare. Eliza was thinking—what a strange destiny was hers. To have become Regent of Paraguay seemed none of her doing but the inevitable result of events that had linked up like chains. She would have preferred to be nearer the theatre of war but Francisco had told her that she could be of more use to him in the capital looking after affairs of State than at Headquarters. Regent of Paraguay! It was an empty title. Everything was decided by Francisco anyway. She was a mere figurehead. She went regularly to church with her children, received the diplomatic corps, supervised the construction of the new Palace and the Opera House, that went on despite the war, and was a patron of several charitable institutions. This morning she was about to pay a visit to the hospital where many of the wounded had been brought from the front. The casualties had arrived in Asuncion in half crippled steamers entirely lacking in medical supplies and food. Hundreds who had escaped death on the battlefield perished on the journey.

The hospital was run by three conscientious, overworked Englishmen Dr. Fox, Dr. Rhind and George Masterman, all three hatchet-faced, lean and sandy haired. Lopez had brought them out from England under contract. Although the hospital was supposed to have three hundred beds, there were three times that number of patients.

Madame Lynch arrived in a carriage accompanied by Senora Martinez and Senora Jovellanos. As they were about to enter the building which smelt of carbolic and pus, the two dames de compagnie asked if they might remain outside because the stench made them feel sick. Eliza gave them a withering look and steeled herself to do her duty. She was met at the entrance to the hospital by the two doctors and their assistant who escorted her through the building. Trailing on Eliza's footsteps came a group of Negro slaves, carrying baskets of provender. To each patient she presented a cantarillo of rum, and a portion of sugar as well as cigars and yerba mate. Some thanked her, some merely stared while others looked at her beseechingly. "Oh, Madama. I am weak, weak. Shall I get better?" She answered reassuring words but the repetitive words kept ringing in her ears as she walked down the wards which seemed to elongate along her path.

The sick lay in rows on primitive cots that were mere strips of hide attached to wooden frames. The visitors stood about in groups at the end of the narrow litters facing their dear ones. In one corner of the ward a patient played a guitar, in another a priest heard confession; in the centre of the floor a soldier whose arm had just been amputated danced a media cana with his sweetheart. Yet in another section of the dormitories a man held a cigar to his lips and blew out the smoke with his dying breath. Eliza crossed herself and instinctively raised her eyes to Heaven and saw that the ceiling was black with cigar smoke. Pona Tobati. Dios lo guarde.

Yet, Eliza knew that these same people who now blessed her would readily cut her throat, even torture her, if the fortunes of war went against her. In this fight to the finish she and Francisco were struggling for their own preservation. She could never expect any mercy from a people in whose language the word "Mercy" did not exist. Eliza was seldom apprehensive but today, after her visit to the hospital, her thoughts were gloomy. What would happen to the children, she wondered, if they lost the war? She must make provision for the future. The Treasury of Paraguay was full. It contained the accumulated gold of three Dictators but they had no reserves abroad. The irony of the situation was that, although she had the wealth of a nation at her disposal, she had nothing that she could call her own. If they were forced to flee the country they would be destitute. And she dared not ask Francisco to send gold out of Paraguay for he would accuse her of lack of patriotism. "Have you no faith in our eventual victory?" he would jeer. "I would not even consider the possibility of defeat." Nevertheless she knew where her duty lay.

Eliza was interrupted in her reflections by dona Juliana Echegaray de Martinez; "My husband has just been gazetted a Captain in the army." She informed her mistress. Eliza raised an eyebrow and feigned an interest that she far from felt. Juliana was a talkative little woman of no great intellect who got on Eliza's nerves.

"Are there any other matters of interest?" asked Eliza a trifle acidly.

The lady in waiting did not need much encouragement. She prattled away gaily. She knew exactly what losses the Argentines had suffered, the position of the Paraguayan troops and the latest gossip at the Court of Rio de Jeneiro.

As her facts had proved correct in the past Eliza was suspicious.

"You seem very well versed."

"My cousin, Jorge Alboniz writes to me from Buenos Aires," she blurted out and then turned crimson.

Eliza pretended not to notice her discomfort. "And pray, how does the information reach you?"

"Oh, through the French Legation," said Juliana brightly. "It is quite easy to get letters past the line. They come addressed to Masterman."

"Really and why Masterman?"

"Because he is a foreigner and a friend of the minister."

Monsieur Laurent-Cochelet, thought Eliza. It was not the

first time that she had crossed swords with the Laurent-Cochelets.

Francisco had left Eliza in Asuncion to feel the pulse of the country. She discovered that the upper classes, interrelated as they were with the old Argentine and Uruguayan families, had no sense of loyalty to Paraguay and indeed would welcome an allied victory. The middle classes or mestizos were only out to make money and exploit the war. The Guarani alone, the true native population, were patriotic and loyal to Francisco Solano Lopez.

At that moment Eliza looked across the square and saw don Saturnino Bedoya, the Treasurer-General get into his carriage. "Where does he go every afternoon?" she asked her companion. "To see his mother-in-law dona Juana Pabla Carillo de Lopez."

That is strange thought Eliza, so do Venancio, Benigno, Rafaela and Inocencia. In the past her instinct had often proved correct and now she smelt conspiracy. On the other hand it was not an accusation she could make before Francisco without definite proof. The Lopez family were sacrosanct in his eyes. Eliza decided to take the law into her own hands.

The following morning she called at the Treasury. The double doors of a series of adjoining rooms were flung open precipitously to allow her to sweep through into the presence of the Treasurer General without prior warning. This privilege was the prerogative of a head of state.

Don Saturnino was seated at his desk, and looked up, surprised to see Madame Lynch stand before him. He rose to his feet and said. "What can I do for you dona Eliza?"

"Don Saturnino, I understand that you have the keys of the vaults in your possession," she said sweetly. "I have duplicates but I would not dream of using them without your permission. I want you to release me four cases of gold coins."

Don Saturnino turned pale. "But that is impossible, dona Eliza, the Treasury has been left in my care and I am answerable to the Marshal-President."

The Minister was a bland and pompous little man. He spat the end of his chewed cigar into a brass spitoon which stood by the side of his desk and, in his agitation, started walking up and down the room. Eliza stood looking out of the barred window watching the market people haggling in the square. "I am not here to argue with you, don Saturnino. You will place at my disposal four cases of bullion," she said in the form of a statement rather than a request. "Perhaps you do not realize that I have been given full and plenary powers by the Marshal-President who has named me Regent of Paraguay. I, and I alone am responsible for my actions."

In a whining voice don Saturnino pleaded. "You do not know what you are asking. It is more than my life is worth to release the gold reserves. Give me a few days. I will send a messenger to Humaita and ask don Francisco's permission."

Eliza looked at him with a glacial expression. "I do not want don Francisco to be molested. He has enough worries on his shoulders."

There was an awkward pause. The shrill cries of the street vendors could be heard in the Minister's office. Don Saturnino began to perspire. "Dona Eliza," he cleared his throat. "I implore you, I beg of you to desist. It is impossible."

"Impossible. Impossible," she gave an irritating little laugh that sent a shudder down his spine. "Do you doubt my good faith? That alone could cost you your life, don Saturnino." Eliza decided to take a chance. "It has come to my knowledge that you have received several letters from General Mitre through the French Legation in Asuncion inviting you to sign a separate peace with the Allies. It is you rather than Benigno or Venancio whom the Argentine Confederation would place as puppet ruler of Paraguay. Dona Juana herself, jealous of her comforts has implored you to accept. You are only waiting to see which way the wind blows. If don Francisco knew of the plot he would not hesitate to have you shot as a traitor and I can assure you that I will not be reticent in revealing the fact should you fail to send me the cases of gold before nightfall."

Eliza picked up her skirts and swept out of the room where it seemed even the walls broke out into a cold sweat.

That same night two dozen slaves carried the chests of gold from the vaults of the Treasury to the old Palace and in the morning Eliza set out with a small retinue and a fleet of pack mules for Humaita. She was glad to leave Asuncion behind her. Eliza Lynch was not made for a life of inactivity when great events were in the offing. They rode through the day and most of the night over fields entangled with stunted tropical vegetation. On her arrival at the fortified position of Humaita on the bend of the river Paraguay guarding the approach to Asuncion, Eliza could see the remnants of the Paraguayan fleet at anchor in the cove, as well as three neutral ships. She sent the cases on board the Italian corvette "La Ardita", and consigned the goods to a M. Jelot of Paris and thought "I may have robbed the Treasury but I have only done my duty."

"What are you doing at Humaita?" the Marshall-President enquired on seeing Eliza ride up to headquarters.

"I have come to join you."

"I left you as Regent."

"Yes," she said, "but I have discovered that the seat of Government is wherever you are, Francisco."

CHAPTER TWENTY-THREE

HUMAITA

ELIZA tried to make the Headquarters of Humaita look less grim by planting flowerbeds of geraniums neatly encased in borders of white-washed pebbles. Lopez occupied one side of the small adobe house, Eliza resided on the other and the Bishop lived between them. If it was different to the rococo palace of Patino or the sombre dwelling in the capital, she felt she was participating in events from which her nature would not allow her to be separated. The four boys were left in Asuncion under the care of Senora Jovellanos and a priest appointed by Bishop Palacios.

One of Eliza's first acts on reaching Humaita was to have a cemetery erected on the hills above the fort for thirteen Englishmen who had lost their lives in the Battle of Riachuelo. The plot of ground was surrounded by a railing and entered through a wrought-iron gate.

In spite of the common occurrence of death all round her she found time to leave flowers on the Englishmen's graves every day.

Cunningham Graham tells us that she was quite fearless. "On several occasions she is said to have exposed her life most recklessly during the siege of Humaita, walking amongst the falling shells, as did the Queen of Naples at the Siege of Gaeta, when her coward husband, Il Re Bamba was sheltering, as did Lopez, behind a shell proof casemate."

In an attempt to recuperate his losses Lopez ordered great barges of men to drift down the river by night as far as Riachuelo and endeavour to rescue the overturned vessels. The crews, dressed in white, their faces grotesquely painted to resemble evil spirits, managed to retrieve the shell of the

Paraguari from under the very noses of the superstitious Macacos and towed her back to Asuncion. Lopez announced this feat as a great victory.

The Marshall then conceived the idea of laying torpedoes in the river. The task was given to a young man by the name of Jaime Corbalan, a member of one of the old familes of Asuncion. Corbalan obeyed instructions and carried the missiles down the stream in a canoe but once he was out of range of the Paraguayan batteries he gave himself up to the Brazilians "to escape," he said, "the tyranny of Lopez."

Francisco Solano was outraged by this blatant treachery and determined to set an example that would act as a warning to anyone else who tried to follow suit. The deserter's mother dona Oliva Corbalan, a highly aristocratic woman, was made to write an article in the Semanario denouncing her son. She was then stripped of all she possessed, including her clothes, and exiled with her four daughters to an Indian settlement where she eventually died. One daughter went mad and the others were reduced to penury.

After a year the war was virtually at a standstill except for daily skirmishes between the Paraguayan gunboats and the Brazilian ironclads. These warships sometimes fired as many as four thousand shells a day on Humaita but they inflicted relatively little damage. The Paraguayan returned their shelling by blowing short blasts on their horns known as "turututus" which if they failed to inflict damage at least showed the Brazilians what they thought of them.

Lopez had a macabre sense of humour. Every afternoon he sent a little steamer called the "Gualeguay" to defy the whole of the Brazilian navy. Like a yapping lap dog she fired her twelve pounder into the middle of the assembled fleet anchored off a sandbank called Itapuru and was answered by every kind of projectile from a 68-pounder to 150-pounder, while the wake foamed and fountained round the little target. Lopez and his Chiefs of Staff looked on from the heights of Humaita and roared with laughter, a merriment that was shared by the volunteers taking part in the exercise. They, more than anyone else, enjoyed teasing the Brazilians. Every day, for three weeks, the little ship made a nuisance of herself until finally she was destroyed.

On the afternoon that the Gualeguay met its fate Eliza walked down the hill to commiserate with the comrades of the crew that had lost their lives. "Yes, we are sad for them," they answered, "because tomorrow they won't be having a good laugh at the Macacos." This utter disregard of death was something that Eliza would never understand.

The Brazilians were among the first people to use a balloon as a means of reconnoitring the position of the enemy. The ascent caused a stir in the Paraguayan ranks. The balloons had been imported from Paris at a cost of 15,000 dollars each and rose to a height of a hundred and ten yards, held by ropes and manned by three men.

Lopez, Madame Lynch and the Bishop stood on a mound to watch the balloon flying in the sky through a telescope. The Bishop was convinced that it was a supernatural phenomena and shook in his shoes. His suspicions were confirmed when the balloon caught fire and he said "It has been stricken by the hand of God. We are saved." But when a second and third went up, which became invisible for a while behind a cloud, he crossed himself several times and declared. "It is indeed unnatural that these men should be given a glimpse of the hereafter before their time. They must have sold their souls to the devil." Lopez ordered large fires to be lit around his positions which not only served as a smoke screen but suffocated the ballonists and that was the last that was seen of the experiment.

Before the war, for the amusement of the children, Lopez and Madame Lynch had ordered from Paris a peep show and a phantasmagoria lantern, such as were to be seen at Fairs in England at the time. The apparatus had duly arrived prior to the outbreak of hostilities but the printed directions which followed were held up by the Allies who were convinced that they were blue prints to some secret weapon. Eliza thinking that a magic lantern show might entertain the troops, asked Colonel Thompson to reassemble the pieces which he did with the help of George Masterman. Once the mechanism was put together a night was chosen and the troops ordered to turn out.

Lopez and Madame Lynch, accompanied by Vicente Barrios, recently appointed Minister of War and Marine, the Bishop and half a dozen aides-de-camp, assisted at the presentation that was held in the patio of an abandoned house. The Marshal-President and his entourage settled down to watch the magic lantern show. They sat in a circle facing a sheet, hung between two courtyards, on to which the slides were projected. The soldiers stood woodenly behind them gazing with wandering attention at coloured etchings from the Illustrated London News. The whole performance was received in stony silence. It was only when the Bishop's shadow appeared across the screen with an elongated nose that the troops broke into paroxysms of mirth, an amusement that was shared by the Marshal-President himself who guffawed until the tears ran down his face.

CHAPTER TWENTY-FOUR

THE BATTLE OF BELLACO

WHEN Lopez wanted information about the position of the enemy he sent a scout to kidnap a sentry posted outside the Allied camp. The unfortunate victim was brought back to headquarters and made to talk. If he proved reticent he was submitted to a little pressure. In this way Lopez learned that a mass concentration of troops was being assembled along the Parana preparatory to an invasion of Paraguay. His informer told him that there were ten thousand Brazilians under General Osorno, ten thousand Argentines commanded by General Mitre and the same number of Uruguayos led by President Flores.

The Allied armies crossed the Parana in force in March 1866, at a point called "El paso de la Patria", where the river is at its most narrow. They made use of every kind of craft from canoes to floating piers and entrenched themselves at Carrizel, the great marshland of Nemburu, which was intersected by lagoons and hummocks known as "albardones". Lopez was irritated but not disheartened because he knew better than the Allies that the Estero Bellaco formed a natural defence. Rather than wait to be attacked the Marshal, never sparing of his troops, put twenty thousand men in the field.

The President held a council of war at his headquarters at Paso Pucu, a thatched hut resting on stilts, and ordered an attack to take place on the morning of the 24th May. He opened a map which he had had prepared of the ground and said "This is where we are and this is where the battle will take place", and pointed with his jewelled baton to a place called "Tuyutay" situated between two branches of the Bellaco river. The stocky figure, in top boots up to his thighs and a plumed helmet, struck the fear of God into his obsequious staff. He entrusted the right flank to General Resquin, the hero of Mato Grosso, who was given eight cavalry regiments and two battalions of infantry. The centre, comprising four battatlions and two regiments, was confided to Colonel Hilario Marco and the left flank entrusted to General Diaz, a man who had risen from the ranks and consequently was a great favourite of Marshal Lopez. General Bruguez was placed in command of the reserve. Marshal Lopez posing like Napoleon with one arm in his doublet said taciturnly; "The plan of campaign is the following—The main body of the army comprising the right, left and centre columns will proceed to take up their positions immediately opposite the Allied lines while General Barrios, in command of the rear guard, composed of six battalions of infantry and two regiments of cavalry will make a detour and surprise the enemy from the back. On reaching their position they will fire a rocket that will act as a signal for all fronts to attack simultaneously . . ."

But Lopez had not reckoned with the difficulties of the terrain. The rear guard was obliged to march in single file and cut their way with pick axes through a forest of pine trees. Consequently instead of attacking the enemy at dawn, as Lopez intended, the rocket was not fired until midday by which time the enemy scouts had reported the movement of troops and the Allies were on the lookout for them.

In the face of events General Barrios should have postponed the battle for a more favourable opportunity but Lopez's word was law and Barrios dared not disobey. Despite these setbacks the Paraguayans fell on the enemy with a frenzy that made the Allies exclaim that Lopez must have given his men gun powder to drink. The Marshal watched the progress of battle from the headquarters. Now one side, now another had the advantage. At one point the Allies advanced in four columns carrying their cooking utensils hoping to reach Humaita by nightfall but they were met by the enfilading fire of the Parguayan batteries which decimated their ranks and struck them down like toy soldiers. In another engagement a force of Parguayan cavalry attacked a sand bank that the Brazilians had fortified. The greater part of the platoon was cut to pieces and the horses swallowed in quicksand. A few survivors got into canoes and struggled home. Those who were wounded in the leg used their arms and those that had lost an arm paddled with their legs.

To the Paraguayan death had no terror. This was a state of mind called ne-nanduco that Lopez knew how to exploit. It was an atavistic legacy inherited from remote ancestors that accepted the inevitable as simply as eating and drinking. Not even the Christian religion responsible for implanting on men's mind a supernatural fear of what should be regarded as a natural phenomena, could supplement this more primitive attitude. Colonel Thompson in his book *"The War in Paraguay"* states, "Officers from the Allied camp wrote from the field of battle that the carnage had been something frightful as no human power could make the Paraguayan surrender and then, even single individuals would rather fight on, with certain death before them." Thompson continues: "A Paraguayan soldier never complained of an injustice and was perfectly contented with whatever his superior demanded—If he was flogged, he consoled himself by saying "If my father did not flog me, who would?" Everyone called his superior officer his father and subordinate, his son."

The Allies suffered a loss of 8,000 men but the Paraguayan casualties were twice that number. After the battle there was a truce while both sides burnt their dead and attended to the wounded. In many instances Lopez ordered that the more severe cases should be put out of their misery. He was severely criticized for this order in the outside world and was accused by the Allies of inhumanity and brutality. But nobody took into account that wounds festered and became gangrenous in a few hours and that he had not the doctors nor the stretcher bearers to give his men proper medical attention.

Neither side could claim a victory but, in the Battle of Bellaco, Lopez lost the flower of Paraguayan manhood despite the fact that several of his Regiments came home wearing looted uniforms and with their pockets full of gold, which they were later made to change into paper currency by Madame Lynch.

CHAPTER TWENTY-FIVE

A TRUCE

On the 10th of September, 1866, the Marshal-President sent a note to the Allied Commander-in-Chief proposing a parley. Both sides were sick of the war and seemed to have reached a deadlock. Francisco hoped that they might come to an agreement and work out honourable terms; so, on receiving a favourable reply to his note, he set out to meet General Mitre, the President of the Argentine Republic. The Marshal looked not unlike Napoleon III in full dress uniform complete with gold spurs and patent leather boots. A high collar of gold lace stood up stiffly from the slit of his scarlet poncho. His Excellency drove to the Allied camp in an American buggy, occupying, like his father, the whole of the back seat while his two corpulent brothers Benigno and Venancio sat opposite to him. Apart from his own personal bodyguard of twenty four tried veterans Lopez was accompanied by his general staff including don Vicente Barrios, his brother-in-law and Panchito his eldest son, a precocious boy who had inherited Eliza's good looks and the Marshal's arrogance. He had refused to stay at home and had joined his parents at Humaita and had come with them to Paso Pucu. Although he was barely twelve he had enveigled his father into giving him a commission in the army and he now wore the uniform of a lieutenant.

When they were within two hundred yards of the enemy lines, Lopez, who was now extremely fat, alighted from the carriage and mounted his favourite cream mare. The cavalcade rode in no set formation but huddled together like sheep. Lopez was so afraid of being ambushed that he ordered a battalion of rifle corps to be hidden in the undergrowth between the Paraguayan and Allied entrenchments. He also took the precaution of choosing a roundabout route to conceal from the enemy the exact position of his headquarters. Halfway towards the meeting place, Lopez felt faint and had to be given brandy.

When in sight of the Allied camp, Mitre advanced to meet him. In contrast to Marshal Lopez's full regalia, the President of the Argentine was very plainly apparelled in undress uniform and an old battered hat, known as a Jim Crow, of which he was very fond.

At a distance of twenty paces the two Presidents drew in their horses and saluted each other ceremoniously with unsheathed swords. They then dismounted and shook hands; chairs were brought and placed in a clearing of the jungle and the combined general staffs retreated some distance, leaving the two Presidents alone. Several Argentine Officers, including General Mitre's two aides-de-camp, took advantage of this temporary truce to visit friends and drink mate behind the Paraguayan lines.

The meeting between the two Presidents lasted five hours. They made speeches at each other and became drunk with their own rhetoric. General Mitre made it clear from the start that he refused to discuss any peace terms unless Lopez was prepared to abdicate. This was in agreement with the Allied pact. On the other hand he knew that it is always wise to build a bridge for a flying enemy and he hinted that Lopez's path would be paved with gold. But what were riches to Lopez without Paraguay? What was Paris without power? Finally the President of Paraguay compromised by saying "I am willing to sail to Europe for two years but at the end of that time I shall return to Paraguay".

It was a way of saving face and making a dignified departure. Mitre was about to concede the point when Lopez drew back. No. No. he thought. Once gone, return might be difficult. The stocky figure drew himself up to his full height. "I will never yield an inch of this sacred soil nor forsake Paraguay except I die." His own egotism would not allow him to accept the conditions laid down by the Allies. Mitre was equally firm and refused to negotiate unless the Marshal agreed to resign. Thus they went round in circles neither one side nor the other giving way.

Without coming to any agreement they agreed to part. The Presidents ceremoniously exchanged riding whips, drank a measure of brandy from each other's hip flask and bade fare-well.

When they were about to take their leave Panchito, with the arrogance of youth, insolently hurled a torrent of abuse at the Allied Commander—for which he was severly repri-manded by his father.

CHAPTER TWENTY-SIX

THE VIRGIN OF CAACUPE

PARAGUAY was like an island completely cut off from the out-side world. The Allies hoped to starve the nation into submission while the Parguayans depended on their own endurance for survival.

Eliza never wavered in her loyalty to Lopez. No matter how desperate the situation appeared, the thought of leaving him never entered her head although she had had ample oppor-tunity to do so. Both at Humaita and Curupaity neutral ships had offered to take her and her children to a place of safety. But she had preferred to stay. Paraguay had become a part of her. It was not so much the people she saw suffering and dying around her, but the blood red earth that would go on forever and for that she was prepared to live and die herself.

Eliza had a scheme that she wanted to put into effect but like all plans it required money. Yet there was untold wealth in this country, she brooded, where gold was merely a bright object and jewels had the value of beans.

That evening, after dinner at headquarters, Eliza drew the Bishop to one side and said "Has glass the same worth as diamonds in the eyes of the Lord"?

"Why, surely, dear lady, the Lord is not concerned with temporal things."

"Then the jewels in the shrine of Our Lady of Caacupe could be replaced with baubles and make no difference to our Lord."

"But that is impossible," said the Bishop genuinely shocked. "The people have sacrificed their jewels as a symbol of their faith."

"Have you not said, my Lord Bishop, that in the Kingdom

of Heaven, it is the spiritual that matters and not the materialistic."

"That is correct," conceded the Bishop. "The value of the articles are intrinsically the same."

"In that case" retorted Eliza "What is there to prevent us from making an exchange. The people will be no wiser and only Paraguay will be the richer."

If the Bishop had any scruples about the transaction he was wise enough to keep them to himself. Two days later Madame Lynch and the Bishop set out on a pilgrimage to the Virgin of Caacupe. They rode on mules at an artificial pace, *portante, andadura, ambladura y sobrepaso,* as ladies and Bishops travelled in Europe in the middle ages. In the heat of the afternoon they began the steep ascent of the Cordillera Azcura. From the summit they looked down on the great lake of Ipacarai to which the Bishop pointed and said, "That blue lake that you see yonder, dear lady, was once a fertile plain but the inhabitants refused to be converted by the Jesuits who brought them the gospel and they preferred to smoke cigars and live in ignorance. The priests, in pious anger, cursed the obstinate heathens and the waters rose flooding the meadows and drowning the dwellers who slept soundly in their hammocks. Only the voice of a parrot was heard calling out "Terri ho, Terri ho. Take heed. Take heed." But the population slumbered on."

"Then what did the Jesuits do to stop the water from rising?" enquired Madame Lynch in her practical way.

"Ah dear lady, they sprinkled Holy Water and God dried His tears."

Towards evening they arrived at the lonely shrine of Caacupe standing in a clearing of the jungle, guarded by one solitary hermit said to be a leper. The Blue Virgin was a miracle-working oracle to whom the faithful brought their jewels in grateful thanks for past favours. Eliza and the Bishop, like two conspirators, dismounted from their mules and entered the small chapel.

Even before Eliza's eyes had grown accustomed to the

partial darkness within the shrine they were dazzled again by the brilliance surrounding the effigy of Our Lady. The Mother of God was covered from head to foot in sparkling diamonds and every kind of precious stone. Her diadem alone, not unlike the crown of the Andes, was worth a King's ransom. Pendants hung from her ears, her fingers were stiff with rings and row after row of priceless pearls had been placed around her slender neck by the devout pilgrims who, when unable to attach another pearl to her person or ornament to her dress, had laid offerings at her feet so that she stood in a sea of jewels.

It was an age old custom for the faithful to ask a question of the oracle and the Virgin either bowed her head in assent or nodded in denial. To be sure of a favourable answer however it was always prudent to give a silver dollar to the hermit, a precaution that the Bishop had already adopted.

Fearlessly Madame Lynch approached the shrine and asked "Our Lady, are you willing to part with your jewels for the sake of Paraguay?"

There was a pause. An angry look passed between the Bishop and the leper. Suddenly the head of the Virgin nodded like a mandarin "Yes. Yes. Yes."

"Our Lady, are you willing to make the sacrifice to ensure peace?" prompted the Bishop.

"Yes. Yes. Yes." answered the Virgin.

"Tell me, Oh Mother of God, shall we win this sacred war?" asked Madame Lynch.

The Virgin seemed to shoot sparks like a Roman candle as she reassured her interrogator. Undoubtedly, the miracle-working Virgin was on the side of Francisco Solano Lopez.

Madame Lynch had come well prepared. With greedy fingers she took the Virgin's crown and then proceeded to denude the image. She unclasped the diamonds, gathered the jewels, relieved the Mother of God of her strings of pearls and drew the rings off her fingers; all of which she placed in a great glittering pile at her feet. Then she dressed the Virgin in one of her own ball gowns which she had brought for that

E

purpose and decorated her like a Christmas tree with strings
of beads and baubles. As she stepped back to admire her
handiwork she said to herself with true Irish logic, "Exchange
is no robbery."

Ever since, visitors have been puzzled that the Virgin of
Caacupe should be dressed as Queen Elizabeth I.

Eliza had made her plans and knew to what purpose she
would devote the treasure. Madame Lynch had decided to
found a Regiment of Women. With this end in view she returned to Asuncion and summoned a great meeting of all
eligible women between the ages of sixteen and forty at the
Campo Grande. Some came reluctantly, some filled with
patriotic zeal, and others with mere apathy but all carrying
banners, *Viva Lopez, Viva Lavinche.* When the recruits were
assembled and formed in rows Eliza Lynch appeared on the
parade ground mounted on a black stallion, accompanied by
her own personal escort of lifeguards. Eliza wore a uniform
reminiscent of the young Queen Victoria but whereas her
Majesty reviewed fresh English faces in Windsor Great Park,
Eliza Lynch was confronted by hordes of ignorant Guarani
women on the plains of Asuncion.

"Women of Paraguay!" Eliza Lynch addressed her subjects, "The Country calls you. If the men are unable to stop
the invading hordes let the women of Paraguay put their
shoulders to the spoke. We must defend our sacred land from
the monkey and the Gaucho. No sacrifice is too great. The
elderly can fend for themselves and the children care for
each other. We must be prepared to leave hearth and home.
On your behalf I will ask the father of our country Taita
Guzu to allow you to serve in his ranks. I speak for all of us
because I, too, am the mother of Paraguayan sons. But our
services and our lives are not enough. We must be prepared to
sacrifice our jewels for the cause."

To this eloquent speech delivered by Eliza in Spanish, the
Guarani women responded and placed their golden trinkets
on the ground at the feet of Madame Lynch's horse. Gold
chains, amulets, ear rings and brooches, not to mention golden

combs, were readily sacrificed for the ultimate glory of the fatherland. The torrent of patriotism was not confined to the Guarani alone but extended to the upper classes who were asked to part with one tenth of their jewelry. Many of the ladies—remembering their premonitions at the dance the previous year when they had been ordered to wear their jewels—looked at each other as much as to say "I told you so."

Regiment after regiment of women were enrolled. Paraguay was the first nation since the days of ancient Greece to have an army of Amazons. The women wore uniforms designed by Eliza consisting of skirts, men's tunics and multi-coloured ribbons in their hair. They were taught their military duties by officers who had been discharged from the army as unfit for military service. The women were drilled and instructed in the use of the lance but not fire-arms because rifles could not be spared. In effect they became a sort of land army living under canvas in large camps between Asuncion and Humaita. They cut down fire wood, worked as road menders, yoked the oxen, drove the plough, slaughtered the animals in the "abattoirs" and acted as camp followers. Francisco, however, kept them in reserves and did not allow them near the front.

On August 31st 1867, The Times (London) reported—
"The women and children are made to work for the army and some of the former are supposed to have fought by the side of the men, as the bodies of several have been found among the heaps of slain. The devotion of the Paraguayan to their leader—whether inspired by love or terror is not very clear—almost surpasses belief."

CHAPTER TWENTY-SEVEN

CHOLERA

PARAGUAY stood with her back to the wall. Slowly the blockade was taking its toll. The people were in need of basic necessities, lack of salt being one of the worst. All sorts of substitutes were tried such as boiling leaves and mixing them with ashes. The besieged Paraguayans used their ingenuity to the utmost. Every kind of experiment was tried. Soap was manufactured in the camps from animal fats. Hides were stretched tight on drums, beaten and scraped and made into clothes for the troops. The soldiers were delighted with the result until the rains drenched the skins and they shrank and became as stiff as cardboard. Masterman tells us that the Aubusson carpets from the club at Asuncion were cut up and fashioned into ponchos for the troops. Wine was distilled from oranges, ink was made from berries and powder was fabricated in the Arsenals of Asuncion, the sulphur being obtained from iron pyrites and the saltpetre from urine and putrid meats. Colonel Trauenfeld, the German Director of Telegraphs found a means of manufacturing paper out of the fibre of "Caraguata", a plant not unlike the wild pine apple. The one commodity that they had in plenty was cotton. The troops were generously provided with shirts and drawers, but what was the use of underclothes in a country that was faced with starvation.

One misfortune seemed to lead to another. Cholera broke out among the troops and the epidemic spread to the civilian population. More than fifty deaths were reported daily. Don Benigno Lopez, the Marshal's elder brother was one of the first victims to be laid low by the disease. General Resquin, known as Shark-face, and Doctor Stewart, the Director-General of the Medical department followed suit. Then, of all people, the Marshal-President himself was striken.

The Minister of War and the General staff were in a panic. At first they decided to keep the matter secret from the troops but the consequences arising from the Marshal's possible demise were too grave to be risked. They felt helpless. The one person who was accustomed to command was too ill to give orders. Without Lopez the Paraguayans were as helpless as children, and to complicate the issue Madame Lynch was away in Asuncion. It was agreed that she must be informed at once. She must be recalled but nobody took the initiative. They dared not telegraph for fear of causing alarm. They were in a quandary. Don Vicente Barrios held a round table conference. Argument shifted backwards and forwards but they failed to reach any decision and in the meantime the President lay dying.

In the capital, Eliza worked far into the night. There were accounts to be looked into. Decisions to be made on the construction of roads. What animals should be slain, what land should be ploughed and what crops should be raised were all items that needed her attention.

Finally, wearily, she put the papers to one side and drew a sheet of paper towards her on which was marked—Palacio Guvermental—Asuncion. Eliza was a bad correspondent but tonight, in spite of fatigue, she decided to write to her mother in Cork. But when she tried to formulate her thoughts there seemed so little to say. Was it of any interest that she was the Mistress of the Marshal-President, that she had four sons, that she sat in a Palace where, instead of marble halls, there were leaking corridors.

As she put pen to paper there was a sound of gravel thrown up at her window. She went on writing. "In spite of being besieged we are confident of our ultimate victory." Eliza was entirely without fear. "Let the rabble murder me if they want to," she thought to herself. There it was again. She got up and angrily flung open the window. To her intense surprise she saw Panchito her eldest son in the street. He was dirty and dishevelled. Beside him stood a panting horse covered in foam.

"Pancho, what are you doing in Asuncion?"

"Mama, come at once. Papa is dying. I had to come and get you. I have ridden a hundred miles in seven hours. My Uncle Vicente and all the officers have lost their heads."

Eliza called the servants who were huddled over a bracero in the patio and gave orders in Guarani. "I am returning to headquarters at once. Prepare baskets of provisions and pack some clothes. Order me the river steamer 'The Salto de Guayra'. It must be ready to sail at midnight." The liberated slaves ran to do her bidding, fearing that the Brazilians were on their doorsteps to enslave them again.

Mother and son walked to the landing stage. The chug-chug of the river steamer could be heard across the open market place working up steam. A few beggars and cripples, huddled together in doorways for warmth, were the only uninterested witnesses of the drama.

Eliza and Panchito boarded the ship and sailed punctually at the stated hour. There was no need for words between them. The urgency was too great. Eliza dared not think what would happen to her and the children if anything should befall Francisco.

At three o'clock on the following afternoon they arrived at the fort of Curupaity where they disembarked and made straight for Paso Pucu about twenty miles to the interior.

On Eliza's arrival she took complete control. She sent for the Minister of War and told him that the troops were to be informed of the President's illness. "If the worst came to the worst, his aims and ideals would remain unimpaired. They would go on fighting until eventual victory was theirs. A council, presided over by the Regent, would carry on the Affairs of State until Panchito was old enough to assume command." Eliza dismissed the Minister of War and sent for Doctor Stewart. He came at once although he was still convalescent after his illness.

The Marshall lay on a camp bed. His bulky frame seemed to make the cot look smaller. The Bishop hovered in the background like a bird of evil omen. Francisco was barely conscious but lucid enough to turn the Bishop out of the room. Weakly he acknowledged Eliza's presence but when he saw Doctor Stewart he became violent and accused him of trying to poison him. "You are in the pay of the enemy. You want to get rid of me. I will have you courtmartialled. I swear that you will die before me" Lopez ranted and raved. After prescribing bromide which Lopez said he refused to take, Stewart left. Madame Lynch followed him as far as the verandah and whispered, "Oh. Doctor, I am so afraid that the President is going to do something for which I shall never forgive him". Then very pointedly she said, "Could you remit £4,000 to my account in Edinburgh". Doctor Stewart hesitated but realizing the obvious implication replied very quietly, "I will comply with your request".

Eliza returned to the patient. Regardless of the danger to herself she nursed him day and night. She sponged his brow, changed his rumpled bedclothes and hung branches of eucalyptus from the ceiling to keep away the mosquitoes, an enemy more deadly than the Allies for they carried the disease. Eliza slept on the floor in snatches. The incessant shelling continued. The house rattled from time to time. She kept guard by his side and would not allow anyone to enter the sickroom from which even her children were excluded. As she sat by his bedside she thought, he might be cruel, debauched, insane but he was Marshal Lopez, the unconquered General, the father of her children, the defender of her adopted country and the man who was her husband in all but name. If she had her life to live again she would not choose it otherwise.

The President lay dying. Doom seemed to descend on Paraguay. In all churches prayers were said for his recovery and special services were held in the camps imploring the will of the Almighty God to spare his life and just as Eliza could not conceive a life without him nor could the simple Guarani.

He might ill-treat them, beat them, even torture them, but he was unquestionably their *Caria Guzu* and had the power of life and death over them. It was as if the fate of Paraguay hung in the balance.

But for once, God answered their prayers. The fever abated and he was declared out of danger. It was only then that Eliza allowed herself to be undressed and slept long and soundly. She awoke grateful to God that she had been given the strength to retribute the high trust that the Marshal had placed in her. Since his illness the bull-necked General seemed to become more dependent on her, confiding his doubts, his suspicions and fears. There was nobody except Eliza that he could trust. One afternoon she said to him, "Francisco, do you know that in your delirium you threatened Doctor Stewart with his life?" Lopez who had a strange sense of humour laughed heartily at the discomfort of the Scotsman and when Eliza told him that on the strength of it she had got Stewart to send £4,000 to Edinburgh to her account, the Marshal's laughter was better than a tonic.

On his recovery the President had a gold medal engraved. It was designed to be the highest order in the land. On one side there was the profile of Eliza Lynch and on the reverse of the coin were the words DEFENSORA PARAGUENSIS.

CHAPTER TWENTY-EIGHT

TE DEUM

LOPEZ returned to the capital for a brief stay to be present at
a TE DEUM held on his birthday 24th July, 1867, to celebrate his recovery from cholera. The High Mass was officiated
by Bishop Palacios at the Cathedral de la Encarnacion and
attended by all the high ranking Officials, including his
brothers and his brothers-in-law don Vicente Barrios the
Commander in Chief and don Saturnino Bedoya, the
Treasurer General. The worm-eaten Cathedral looked as if
it was about to cave in with the weight of the throng which
included stray dogs and baskets of live chickens. In the church
the sexes were segregated. The officers in dress uniforms
stood to the right of the aisle and the women to the left.
Madame Lynch knelt on a prie-dieu, towering over her sisters-
in-law, Inocencia and Rafaela, and her two ladies-in-waiting.
All five of them wore black mantillas but, whereas the Paraguayan women appeared dumpy and insignificant, Eliza
Lynch looked like the Velasquez portrait of the Lady in Lace.
George Masterman, the English apothecary who was present,
describes her appearance in the following words, "She was a
tall and remarkably handsome woman, and although time
and climate had then somewhat impaired her beauty, I would
well believe the story that when she landed in Asuncion, the
simple natives thought her charms were of more than
earthly brilliancy and her dress was so sumptuous that they
had no words to express the admiration they both excited."

As the President left the Cathedral he was given a tremendous ovation by crippled veterans. Lopez, whom they
worshipped, was never at a loss for words and pointing to the

church said in Guarani; "Have you been in there, my children?"

"Yes, Carai Guzu."

Then pointing to the Bishop, who stood just behind him he said:

"And have you been listening to his words?"

"Yes, Carai Guzu."

"Then don't. Listen to me."

It was a joke and they laughed for days.

The thanksgiving service was followed by a levée at the unfinished Palace of Asuncion which Lopez was anxious to display. The lofty chambers were as yet unfinished but showed promise of great magnificence to come. That cement dusted their clothes or that they went in fear of being killed by the scaffolding did not worry Marshal Lopez. The President stood on a raised dais directly below an immense dome and addressed the assembled company. He delivered a grandiloquent oration hoping that his words would echo as far as Europe and America. After the speech don Saturnino Bedoya replied with an equal degree of eloquence. He lauded the President to the skies and presented him with a Marshal's baton encrusted in jewels, two flags embroidered in gold thread and an album containing a roll of honour bound in massive gold. Lopez received the gifts from the hands of his brother-in-law with a certain asperity.

Then pointing to the Treasurer General he said to the Guard that sent a cold shiver down the spine of all those present, "Arrest that man."

There was general consternation. One or two women screamed. In a voice of thunder Francisco Solano continued, "I charge you with having robbed the Treasury. There are four cases of gold missing from the vaults."

Rafaela screamed and threw herself at Eliza's feet. "Save him. Save him. I implore you."

Eliza looked coldly about her. "Your brother knows what he is about," is all she said.

For a moment there was general pandemonium. The heads

of Foreign Missions tried to intercede with the Marshal-President on behalf of the Treasurer General. Lopez cut them short. "Take him away."

Bedoya struggled to be heard. "Senora Eliza, Senora Eliza," he implored. "Tell them the truth."

Eliza stared haughtily at him until he lowered his gaze. "Nobody, don Saturnino, likes to hear the truth," and she walked proudly out of the Assembly Hall.

The Regent of Paraguay knew he would not speak for he could only implicate himself further.

The Treasurer General was taken away and tortured but in the process his spine was dislodged and he died; a fact that infuriated Lopez because he could not go on tormenting him. Bedoya was one of the first victims to fall in the new reign of terror.

Not so long after their return to Paso Pucu, Lopez turned round to Eliza and said to her apropos of nothing, "By the way, what was there in those boxes that you sent out of the country?"

After a pause the Irish woman answered fearlessly, "Francisco you know as well as I do because nothing happens in this country which is not reported to you."

Francisco Solano laughed from his belly.

"I suppose that you are aware that don Saturnino was in league with the enemy," said Eliza coldly.

"I suspected it for a long time but had no definite proof. That is why I charged him with stealing the Treasury, knowing all the time that you had done it; and now the idiot has gone and died and I am no nearer to ascertaining the truth."

Lopez, like Francia before him, was fast becoming suspicious of his own shadow. People found themselves thrown into prison on the slightest pretext and the most innocent remark was held against them. Alternating between optimism and depression, he instituted the most ingenious system of espionage, whereby every third man was charged to spy on his neighbour and given the authority to shoot at sight if the individual for whom he was responsible showed the slightest cowardice. Thus the whole army from the Generals down to the common soldier distrusted each other. It was a complex mechanism, refined in its subtleties; not even the Confessional was safe.

Commenting on the extreme measures that Lopez adopted to evolve his secret service, Colonel Thompson says, "Lopez was continually in great fear of being assassinated and at night had a double cordon of sentinels round his house. This was afterwards increased to a treble one. During the day they were removed and the guard was kept under an open roof next door. One evening I was waiting to see Lopez, as were several officers, and a Sergeant of the Guard entered into conversation with me. After a short time there was a great stir and the other officers waiting were all arrested. One of Lopez's aides de camp came and said to me, "His Excellency sends word to you to write all conversation you have had with the Sergeant of the Guard and bring it tomorrow." Colonel Thompson did as he was told but by then the Sergeant was dead and the rest of the Guard had received a hundred lashes each. On requesting an explanation Thompson was informed that the Sergeant had been implicated in a plot to murder Lopez, which he found strange because all that he had said was, "Does Queen Victoria wear her crown when she goes out."

Lopez's temper was uncontrollable and his actions were unpredictable, but he had an undeniable magnetic power. The people fully believed him to be their only salvation, convinced that without him they were doomed to death or slavery at the hands of the Brazilian hordes.

CHAPTER TWENTY-NINE

PEACE PROPOSAL

AFTER Marshal Lopez's eloquent appeal to Great Britain, France and the United States, the British Foreign Office decided to send a Government Official to investigate conditions in that besieged country and to evacuate the British subjects —surgeons, draughtsmen, mechanics, merchants and engineers—who were rumoured to be undergoing great hardship.

In September 1867 Mr. Gould, the Secretary at the Legation in Buenos Aires, a fair-haired, serious young man, obtained permission to pass the blockade and arrived at Humaita on H.M.S. "Dotterel". As soon as the ship had dropped anchor, Commander Michelle, accompanied by three aides-de-camp, went ashore to pay his respects to the Marshal-President and to announce the fact that Mr. Gould, her Britannic Majesty's representative was on board. Lopez was immediately on his guard. "I cannot be expected to take any official notice of his visit unless he brings letters of credence but," he said magnanimously, "I will receive him privately".

When young Mr. Gould arrived at the small house at Paso Pucu he was surprised to find Madame Lynch waiting to receive him instead of the President. He had been led to believe that she was a vulgar whore; instead he found a most refined, cultured woman of the world whose courage he could not help admiring. Almost her first words were, "What does Britain intend to do to help us?"

"Britain has the greatest admiration for the tenacity of Marshal Lopez."

"That is not enough. We need ships, arms and ammunition."

"I will inform my Government, Ma'am, which is at present more concerned with the welfare of the British subjects in Paraguay."

At that moment Lopez came strolling into the room smoking a cigar and could not help overhearing the last remark.

"I am sorry that you have been given this mission, Mr. Gould, because I cannot allow you to take one without taking them all— not even to please her Britannic Majesty herself. It may interest you to know that I have just refused a similar request to the American Minister. Besides, I can assure you that none of them has the slightest cause for complaint. They are one and all perfectly happy."

To which Mr. Gould replied, "If the British subjects are as happy and as contented as you say, Sir, then the number of those wishing to leave will be so insignificant as to cause your Government no embarrassment, while you would thus, by a very small sacrifice, gain over to your side not only her Majesty's Government but public opinion in the United Kingdom which has become interested in their fate".

"I will give you every facility to talk freely with any English person in my camp and if you have anything further to communicate on this subject perhaps you will write to Major Caminos, my secretary, who will be instructed to deal with this matter. And now Mr. Gould it would give us much pleasure if you were to honour us with your presence at dinner."

During the meal at which they were joined by the Bishop and the four boys, Lopez and Madame Lynch made themselves particularly affable to the young Englishman. They flattered him and piled up his plate with delicacies. He would be able to see for himself that there was no shortage of food in Paraguay, at least at Lopez's table; and when a plum pudding, made by Madame Lynch's own hands, was served, he was completely won over.

As soon as Mr. Gould had returned to the Dotterel for the night, Lopez sent for Doctor Stewart and said, *"Cuidadoi Si yo sepa que algun Ingles diga que quiere salir del pais;* Beware if it should come to my knowledge that any Englishman says that he wishes to leave the country." Then knowing that Doctor Stewart was a wealthy man, and remembering the cholera incident, he said, "I am taking advantage of Mr. Gould's visit to allow the British subjects to send money out of the country. Perhaps you would like to avail yourself of this opportunity, and while you are about it, you can send £11,000 on my behalf".

In spite of assurances to the contrary, Mr. Gould was unable to meet any British subject in private. Always, Paraguayans were present. Invariably the English stated that they were satisfied with their lot and none of them expressed a desire to leave the country. Mr. Gould was not deceived. In his official despatch to Mr. Mathew Buckley in Buenos Aires he wrote,

"The whole country is ruined and all but depopulated. The cattle in most of the estates have entirely disappeared. The slaves, of whom there were still forty thousand, have been emancipated, the males sent to the army and the females, with other women, forced to work in gangs for the Government.

"Many estates have been altogether abandoned. The scanty crops raised by women are monopolized for the supply of the troops. The women have been obliged to part with all their jewels and gold ornaments, this extreme measure being called a patriotic offering on their part.

"These epidemics, measles, smallpox and cholera, besides privations of all sorts, have deprived the population of this unfortunate country by more than a third. The horses have nearly all died off and the few hundred which yet remain are so weak and emaciated they can scarcely carry their riders.

"The mortality amongst the children has been dreadful and both scurvy and itch are very prevalent. The trade with Bolivia is insignificant owing to the almost insuperable difficulties of communication."

Undaunted, Mr. Gould made an official request, on behalf of Her Majesty's Government, to remove the British subjects from Paraguay. The formal request was written in French on the insistence of Lopez, who spoke the language fluently* and Gould ended his despatch by saying . . . "En outre il y a des femmes et des veuves d'Anglais, chargees d'enfants, qui ne doivant continuer a rester sans exposées aux perils de la guerre."

Lopez sent for him and took pleasure in picking out the grammatical errors. He suggested that "Et surtout" should be inserted instead of "En outre", a point that Mr. Gould was bound to concede. Satisfied that he had scored off the Englishman, Lopez leant back on his chair and pretended to take the young Secretary into his confidence and said, "It is my firm opinion that I have been very badly treated by Great Britain". He complained bitterly of the lack of sympathy and said, "My one desire is to maintain friendly relations with the Queen". Finally he mentioned the breaches of neutrality committed by her Majesty's Government. Putting his hand to his heart in a dramatic gesture he said, "I have unfortunately no one to advocate my cause shut out, as I am, from the rest of the world, but I consider it very unfair on the part of Her Majesty's Government to call upon me to give up the small number of British subjects who have freely entered my services while no notice seems to taken of loans, ships and arms obtained by my adversaries in Great Britain, and of the hundreds of Englishmen fighting against me in their ranks. Yet you may tell Her Majesty that as a token of my good faith and to show that Paraguay is a civilized nation I am allowing you to take the women and children out of the country".

Mr. Gould congratulated him on his humane attitude and found himself offering to mediate between Lopez and the Allies. "I will go to the camp, Sir, and get the best possible terms. I am confident that a satisfactory solution can be found. It is of no advantage to either side to prolong this massacre indefinitely." Besides he made it clear without saying so in so many words that the "Dotterel" would take the Marshal and his family to a neutral port.

*Lopez and Madame Lynch usually spoke French in private.

Lopez brooded. He felt as if he was about to sign his own death warrant. He was slowly being sucked into a morass of bloodshed, want, misery and desolation. How much longer could he reckon with the people's loyalty he wondered. The upper classes would willingly stab him in the back, the middle classes were only interested in profiteering; he could only count on the gentle Guarani and they had almost been eliminated in the death-rattle of the nation. Where, he asked himself had he heard these sentiments before? Yes, it was Eliza who had found this out in Asuncion. It was better that he should depart with honour than face ingratitude. He shut himself in his room for two days and prayed. He smoked endlessly causing his teeth to decay and turn black. Then he sent for Caminos, his secretary, and dictated the following terms: —

1. A secret and previous understanding will assure to the Allied powers the acceptance by the Government of Paraguay of the proposals they are inclined to make.

2. The Independence and integrity of the Republic of Paraguay will be formally recognized by the Allied powers.

3. All questions relating to Territory and limits in dispute before the present war will be reviewed for future consideration, or submitted to the arbitration of Neutral powers.

4. The Allied forces will retire from the territory of the Republic of Paraguay and the Paraguayan troops will evacuate the positions held by them in the territory of Brazil as soon as the conclusion of peace is assured.

5. No indemnity for the expenses of the war will be demanded.

6. Prisoners of war will, on one side and the other, be immediately placed at liberty.

7. The forces of Paraguay will be disbanded with the exception of the number necessary for the maintainance of order, in the interim, of the Republic.

8. His Excellency the Marshal-President at the conclusion of peace or the preliminaries thereof, will retire to Europe, leaving the Government in the hands of the Vice-President,

who according to the Constitution of the Republic remains in charge in similar cases.

Lopez lay back wearily on his hammock. He was sick of the whole business. Let them proceed without him. At least he, the Marshal-President had dictated terms which were honourable to Paraguay and he would be leaving his country with flying colours in a British Man of War. He was not the first Dictator to be faced with abdication.

Francisco dared not think of the weary years ahead when he would join the ranks of other exiled rulers and politicians in Paris. At least Eliza would be pleased to return to France. She had been very patient. It had not been easy for her in Paraguay. He was certain that at the back of her mind she had always wanted to return to France. Besides, it was only fair to his children to spare them the ravages of war and give them a good education. In the meantime he impressed on Caminos the need for the greatest secrecy.

Two days later Mr. Gould, carrying the peace proposals, departed on H.M.S. Dotterel for the Allied Headquarters to meet Marshal Caxias, the Commander in Chief of the combined forces, who had replaced President Mitre when the latter had been recalled to Buenos Aires to suppress a revolution.

The Secretary of the British Legation was received with great civility. The plans were sent to Rio de Janeiro for the approval of the Emperor and everyone was thankful that the war seemed to be over.

But no sooner had the "Dotterel" sailed with Mr. Gould on board, that Madame Lynch stormed into Lopez's presence. "Francisco, what would the Brazilians say, if as a preliminary to a truce you should demand the abdication of the Emperor. No. No. A thousand times No."

With an imperious air, Eliza Lynch summoned Caminos and commanded him to send a despatch at once to Mr. Gould saying that the eighth clause could not even be considered. Instead, Eliza Lynch dictated the following paragraph, "for the rest I can assure you that the best guarantee for the future of "MY COUNTRY" is that Marshal Lopez should follow the lot which God has in store for the Paraguayan nation. The Republic of Paraguay will never stain its honour and glory by consenting that the President and its Defender, who has fought for its existence and made countless sacrifices should descend from his post, and still less that he should suffer expatriation from the scene of his heroism".

Lopez's eyes filled with tears of gratitude, and all he could do was murmur "Mi destino. Mi destino. I bow before my destiny".

When Lopez's resolution to carry on the war was made manifest, Gould returned to Buenos Aires indignant that his efforts in the cause of peace should have been in vain and that all he had been able to save were three women and five children.

The following report was published in *The Times* in London and in the *New York Times* regarding the progress of the war—

The Paraguayan War

Nothing in the history of modern warfare is more remarkable than the extraordinary and almost unparalleled devotion to Lopez displayed by the Paraguayans. That singular race isolated from their neighbours by traditional restrictions accustomed to self sacrifice by the austerity of the Jesuit training and proud of their comparatively pure nationality as contrasted with the heterogeneous mixture of races to be found in the ranks of their opponents regard their President-General with something little short of religious awe and receive his orders civil and military in a spirit of unquestioning obedience. Whatever faults or deeds of cruelty may be urged against Lopez it is impossible to maintain that he rules by mere arbitrary power or terrorism. No personal Government based on such a foundation could have stood the strains to which that of Lopez has been subjected. It is to be hoped that the time for mediation cannot be far off. The Allies must see the impossibility of achieving their object without simply destroying the Paraguayan race from the face of the earth. And even supposing that they are prepared to attempt and able to accomplish this the blood and treasure which they would have to expend would be utterly out of proportion to the stake at issue. Their honour must be satisfied by the material triumphs they have gained in the face of the most heroic resistance and we can not help believing that judicious joint diplomatic action on the part of two or three powers might put an end to a most sanguinary and uncalled for struggle.

New York Times

CHAPTER THIRTY

THE FALL OF HUMAITA

LOPEZ's military position was untenable and he decided to withdraw to the Andes where he hoped that he could prolong the struggle indefinitely, or at least until the Allies quarrelled amongst themselves and returned home. The troops were evacuated from Paso Pucu and the guns at Curupaity were removed by night and logs put in their place. Lopez, with his family, and the entire army numbering about eight thousand men, crossed the river in canoes and successfully succeeded in evading the Brazilian patrols. They landed at a place called Timbo and from there struck for San Fernando, a hundred miles north of the capital, which they reached in about three days taking the hazardous route through the Gran Chaco. The movement was so swiftly executed, and with such secrecy, that the Allies were completely thrown off the scent.

Every time the Brazilian scouts looked through their telescopes they could see troops constantly massed in front of the fort of Curupaity. When, finally, they decided to attack, they found an empty shell and what they had taken to be guns were no more than mere dummies. To add insult to injury, a torpedo that Lopez had laid in the river some months previously went off belatedly and sank the Rio de Janeiro, Brazil's most powerful ironclad.

One by one the forts along the river Paraguay fell to the Allies. Now that Curupaity was in their hands they were free to proceed to Humaita. To cover his hasty retreat to the North, Lopez had left a scanty force in this last great fort, guarding the approach to Asuncion. Four hundred hollow eyed and blue chinned soldiers faced an army of thirty thousand men. Colonel Martinez and Captain Alen sent a desperate message to Lopez saying that the troops had eaten their last horse and were keeping alive on the roots of plants. The answer came back, "Hold out for five more days and then retreat." Maddened with the heat, the humidity, and the smell of putrefaction exuding from the rotting corpses of men and horses, Alen tried to commit suicide. He failed to blow out his brains and succeeded in damaging an eye instead.

Humaita lay shrouded in mist through which loomed a ruined church leaning perilously against a background of tall palm trees. The incessant bombardment was answered by the chattering of parrots and the swishing wings of startled wimorants. Then an ominous silence fell on the place.

The Allies convinced the place had been abandoned were determined not to be fooled for a second time and advanced boldly. When they were within twenty yards of the fort they were met with a thunderous volley of artillery. In a panic they turned tail and fled leaving the Victors, too weak to raise a feeble cheer, lying exhausted among the ruined batteries. But it was only a temporary victory. The besieged eyed each other suspiciously. Their pangs of hunger were such that even thoughts of cannabalism entered their minds; and still they rejected every offer to surrender. At last, through the insistence of a priest, Colonel Martinez raised a flag and the gallant defenders of Humaita capitulated.

"Adelante! On. On. To the North." was Lopez's cry. The remnants of what had been the most disciplined army in South America marched barefoot through swamps that were deep, treacherous and slimy. The stragglers were poorly clothed, ill-fed and weary. They marched by day and, at night threw themselves on the ground beside camp fires that barely warmed their thin blood. The only advantage that the Paraguayans had over the Allies was the fact that they were unencumbered with tents, wagons, arms and ammunition.

After the fall of Humiata Colonel Alen, though suffering from his self-inflicted wound, contrived to escape with a handful of survivors and waded across the Chaco, avoiding the dunes of quicksand until they reached headquarters. It would have been better for these messengers of evil tidings if they had left their bones to be eaten by the jackals at Humaita. They were tortured and after being made to confess that they had sold the garrison to the Brazilians placed before the firing squad and shot.

Lopez held a meeting of his officers outside his tent. His mood was that of a maniac. He looked Negroid in his rage. "I cannot trust any of you. You are all incompetent. You are irresponsible. Time and time again you let me down. I have no faith in you. I stand alone. I stand alone." He kept repeating and thumping his chest. With unreasonable fury he arrested Juliana, Eliza's constant companion and wife of Colonel Martinez, the man responsible for the surrender of the fort who was now a prisoner in Buenos Aires. Juliana was a harmless little chatterbox whose only crime was empty-headedness.

Senora Martinez clung to Eliza's skirts. "Save me. Save me, I implore you." Eliza shrugged her shoulders. No one had thought of her when she was a stranger in a foreign land. Nobody had shown her compassion. She had been ostracized, ridiculed and insulted for eight long years. Why should she waste her pity on the people who had slighted her?

"Senora Eliza, have mercy. I beseech you. I am innocent."

"Are you?" queried Eliza Lynch sweetly. "And how can you explain the letters you have received by diplomatic bag?"

"But they came from my cousin in Buenos Aires."

"So you admit that you have been in communication with the enemy."

"And to whom were those letters addressed?" thundered Lopez.

"To Masterman."

"The assistant surgeon at the hospital?"

Juliana nodded.

"Masterman. Masterman. Masterman. Arrest him,' shouted Lopez. "And take this criminal away, put her in the cala-bozo."

"Have mercy, Senora Eliza." Juliana made one last desperate appeal.

Madame Lynch hardened her heart. Senora Martinez was dragged away crying and screaming. Both the wife and the mother of Martinez, the defender of Humaita were shot as traitors and Masterman, the English apothecary, was arrested as an accomplice.

CHAPTER THIRTY-ONE

THE CONSPIRACY

LA SENORA PRESIDENTA, the name by which Lopez's mother was known was short, buxom, swarthy and asthmatic. She lived at "La Trinidad", the quinta where she had been born and where she hoped to die. From her balcony she could see the shady gardens of Lavinches' Patino but she had never set foot therein. She felt helpless and afraid. She gazed about her in a myopic way as if seeking the presence of one who was no longer there. Where was this son she loved? This man, whom they called Marshal Lopez was not the Francisco that she knew. He was a stranger. She mourned him as if he were dead. Hail Mary. Mother of God. Surely he has been possessed by the evil one. To complain against the tyranny of Lopez was equivalent to death. Viva Lopez! Of course the real person to blame was Lavinche, that French concubine whom Francisco had imported from Paris. It was she, with her greed and love of money, that had brought the country to ruin. She had warned her husband. Don Carlos should have taken her advice and got rid of her years ago.

Dona Juana Pabla sighed. She knew not who were her friends nor who were her enemies. All looked upon each other with suspicion. Even she the mother of the President was no exception. No one was safe. She dared not talk. It was as if the very orange trees had ears and thoughts were visible. Yet there was something that must be said. There were nets within nets. The very name of Paraguay meant a net in Guarani. Where was the laughing country of Carlos Antonio Lopez? It had vanished and become a strange land of shadows, doomed and desolate.

Widespread rumours said that the Allies were about to take Asuncion. It was a miracle that they had not already done so. No doubt Our Lady had intervened. Dona Juana was slow and ponderous in her movements, even her thoughts were apathetic but once she had made up her mind she was resolute. She sent for her daughters Inocencia and Rafaela. Both ladies were reclining on hammocks in the inner patio and swinging themselves gently to and fro. Inocencia was trying to comfort her sister Rafaela whose husband don Saturnino had been tortured to death. Rafaela cursed the Monkey-tiger as she called her brother. "He is a fiend, a devil incarnate. May Satan claim him."

The two women answered their mother's summons. Whining and lachrymose they entered the house and went and sat with dona Juana in the darkened drawing room where no windows were ever opened nor the sun allowed to penetrate for fear its rays might fade the silken hangings. Oil lamps burnt in the middle of the day.

During the course of the afternoon the Senora Presidenta sent a sewing woman with a note to Mr. Washburn asking him to call on her.

The American Minister had only recently arrived back in Paraguay after a short leave of absence in the United States. He had encountered great difficulty in returning to his post because the Allies had hindered his progress and he had been kept hanging around Corrientes for nearly a year. Finally he had embarked on the U.S. battleship *Franklin* determined to force the blockade; and the Allies rather than be involved in a diplomatic incident, had allowed him to proceed.

Washburn was a God fearing man but no diplomat. His good intentions were spoilt by an unfortunate manner and he was too honest to ingratiate himself with Madame Lynch.

Shortly after resuming his position in Asuncion he volunteered to visit Marshal Caxias and obtain the best possible terms for Paraguay. This was the third attempt at mediation and he set off for the Allied camp convinced of his new power of persuasion. But Washburn fared no better than his predecessors. Lopez always felt that Washburn, as a representative of a great nation, could have exerted more pressure and imposed conditions on the Allies. From then on he nursed a grievance, barely tolerating the Minister and waiting for a chance to get even with him. Washburn was of course too thick-skinned to realize that he was an object of Lopez's derision, and continued on the friendliest terms with the Senora Presidenta and the other members of Lopez's family. At least once a week he visited Benigno with whom he played malilla, a form of whist. Don Jose Berges, the Minister for Foreign Affairs and Senor Letite Pereira, the Portuguese Consul, made up the numbers at the card table. At these sessions Washburn was thoroughly indiscreet and openly criticized Lopez and his conduct of the war. His unrestrained language and blunt speech were undiplomatic to say the least, and experience should have taught him that any conversation was reported back to Lopez.

During the hot summer months the American Minister and his family moved out of Asuncion and stayed at a house that had been lent to him by Senora Inocencia Lopez. No doubt the wife of General Barros thought that his presence might serve as a protective influence in the face of a Brazilian invasion. The house that he occupied was not far from the country property of the Senora Presidenta.

Mr. Washburn read the note and wondered what the old lady wished to see him about. He called for a pony trap and departed carrying a red despatch box containing his confidential papers, which he did not like to leave around for fear of prying eyes.

On his arival at the Quinta, where he had been a frequent visitor in the past, Washburn strolled unannounced into the drawing room, expecting to find the Senora Presidenta alone. To his surprise and discomfort, he was confronted by the sight of the old lady seated on a settee, flanked by her daughters.

Behind the matriarch, like figures in a Victorian photograph album, stood her sons, Benigno and Venancio, two fat unprepossessing creatures. Nor did they complete the picture. There was don Jose Berges, the Minister of Foreign Affairs, doddering and suffering from premature senile decay, don Vicente Barrios, the Minister of War, greasy and pompous and lastly the effete figure of the Bishop wearing an amethyst cross round his neck and holding in his bony fingers an ivory crucifix. For a long time no one spoke and all averted their gaze as if unable to look each other in the eye. Their thoughts seemed to will Mr. Washburn to say something conclusive that would put an end to this brutal carnage.

The American cleared his throat. He was too forthright an individual to have patience with innuendos. "You all know the terms of the treaty", he said, "Marshal Caxias will not even consider the possibility of a truce unless . . ." His voice trailed away.

Then in a quiet voice the Presidenta recited. "My name is Juana Pabla Carrillo. I come of an honourable family of Asuncion. My forbears were Spanish, who settled in Paraguay many centuries ago. Sons, daughters and friends, forgive me for what I am about to say but I can no longer keep it to myself. When I was very young I was seduced by my stepfather, an otherwise honourable human being. To make up for the great wrong he did me, and to give my unborn child a name, he affianced me to a man of humble origin but noble of heart. That man was Carlos Antonio Lopez, the best husband that any woman could have asked for. He used the great fortune that came to me to better his position, and so well did he administer the estate that in a few years he became the President of the Republic, and well, you know the rest. He was not one to make a difference between Francisco Solano and the other children who were of his flesh and blood. Indeed if he showed any preference it was to the boy that was not of his seed. But in his last will and testament which has been so cruelly distorted, he entrusted the nation to his primogeniture. Sons, daughters and friends, let me testify here and now that Francisco Solano was not his firstborn. The eldest son of Carlos Antonio Lopez was Benigno and it is he who should have inherited the Presidency of Paraguay".

Benigno broke into a cold sweat and wiped away the beads of perspiration from his pallid face with his delicate hands that were too small for his fleshy body.

The Senora Presidenta continued in a lifeless, asthmatic voice, "Now that I have told you the truth, I trust that you will know how to proceed. May the Lord give us the strength to do what must be done."

"Amen,"reiterated the Bishop. Those assembled departed in silence like conspirators.

A few hours later, as the last post sounded dismally in the camp, Bishop Palacios dismounted from his mule and made his way to Lopez's tent. "May I come in?" he said in the most ingratiating manner. Lopez and Eliza were alone. They sat playing draughts in the light of a solitary candle. The Bishop crossed himself several times. "I have a matter of the greatest consequence to report." Then with a sly look he proceeded to give them a word for word account of the proceedings that afternoon.

Lopez stood up aghast. He shook with uncontrollable rage. He threw himself on the ground, demented, foaming at the mouth and bellowing like an animal. The spasm passed but not his wrath. "I, a Bastard? I, a Hybrid? I, Francisco Solano Lopez, Marshal-President of Paraguay, ridiculed by my sisters, accursed by my brothers and betrayed by my mother. Woman! Whore!" he spat. "Thou shalt not escape."

He ordered the immediate arrest of his mother, brothers, sisters and all connected with the plot. Washburn alone, he dared not touch for fear of infringing International law. "But he will not escape. I will strike him down. May God consume him. To think that my own mother should revile me."

Eliza sat with pursed lips. For years she had had to endure the insults of this woman who had persistently ignored her; and now, at last, had come the hour of retribution. Revenge was sweet.

Francisco shouted at the scared Aide de Camp, "Show no mercy. Treat them like common criminals."

Madame Lynch looked at the Bishop. He smiled but the smile froze on his lips as Lopez shouted, "And shoot that man. Not even his cloth will protect him for daring to denounce my mother."

CHAPTER THIRTY-TWO

RETREAT TO THE NORTH

LOPEZ returned to Asuncion and ordered the evacuation of the city. Let the Allies advance. Let them take Asuncion. Had not Napoleon invaded Russia and found Moscow but an empty shell? He would pursue a scorched earth policy, North. He could drive the population before him. He would compel the allies to follow him into the interior, that vast virgin territory, so weakening their lines of communication. Except for the aged and infirm no one was permitted to remain in Asuncion. The simple people were ordered to leave their homes at a moment's notice. Household goods and chattels were piled high on bullock carts, wheel-barrows and donkeys or carried on the head. A tropical rain fell incessantly on the fleeing refugees, who were terrorized by stories of atrocities should they fall into the hands of the Macacos. Towards evening only dogs looking like jackals slunk about the empty streets.

Lopez looked sadly on Asuncion for the last time. Asuncion, where he had hoped to be crowned Emperor of South America, King of the River Plate. Past were his dreams of balls, stars, uniforms and medallions. Past? No. Only postponed. Viva Lopez. Where were the crowds acclaiming him along his Royal progress? All he could hear were the rumble of wheels as his carriage sped over the uneven roads. Madame Lynch followed with her children in a closed vehicle. They were strongly protected by a mounted escort. At the head of the river a wide panorama came into view. The vast Palace surmounted by a dome, stood reflected in the water, an unfinished monument yet imposing by the enormity of its conception. Beside the Palace, there was a huge opera house, aping the Scala of Milan. "It, too, was never finished," wrote Washburn, "and the only singers were the parrots that trilled their arias in the empty cavern."

When Washburn got the order to remove his Legation to Luque, the temporary capital to the North, he refused to leave Asuncion, the excuse being that his wife was expecting a baby. The President in spite of his personal antipathy, could hardly insist on his order being carried out without offending the great Republic from the North. Then Washburn foolishly asked for the release from prison of Masterman, the young English physician, to attend his wife in her forthcoming confinement.

"He must be out of his mind. Masterman. The accomplice of Senora Martinez?"

"No. Merely a scapegoat in the hands of M. Laurent-Cochelet, who used his name as a screen for Senora Martinez and to get her letters through the lines."

"Then the man is a spy."

"No. A simpleton. Release him, Francisco. We can make better use of him than M. Laurent-Cochelet."

"Laurent-Cochelet. Laurent-Cochelet. Cochon—Cochelet." Lopez spat.

Nine months previously the young English apothecary had found himself thrown into prison, accused of receiving letters that had come through the Allied lines by diplomatic bag. As this was not a crime in itself he was at a loss to understand why he should be punished. In his book "Seven Years in Paraguay", Masterman describes the scene. "As soon as Gomez saw me" (Gomez was the Chief of Police) "he shouted"— "I order you under arrest".

"Indeed Senor," said I. "Why? and until when?"

"That you will know tomorrow."

Masterman goes on to say "I told them that I was aware that ignorance of the law did not excuse its evasion but I neither knew that there was any such regulation concerning the delivery of letters nor had I ever broken it. I considered that I had a perfect right to receive them from M. Cochelet for they had been sent to me under a flag of truce with despatches by the French Secretary of Legation and brought to Paso Pucu by the Consul himself. Moreover I had received many letters, official and private from Humaita and Paso Pucu, many forwarded by the Mayor de Plaza himself, others by the Captain of the Port and none of them had ever passed through the post office or been stamped."

With every word that Masterman uttered he was condemning himself.

"Have you the letters?" Masterman was asked. He answered in the affirmative.

"Take care of them" said the Chief of Police with an ominous ring to his voice.

His narrative continues: "A squad of men with fixed bayonets came to the door and I was marched off between them, through the guard room, across the great courtyard and through a narrow passage into a cell, on the floor of which a candle was burning. And then the full horror of my position burst upon me. I was a prisoner." He goes on to say "I knew at the time of my arrest that this affair of the letters was but a pretext for punishing me, for I had been warned by an influential friend that I had fallen into disgrace, and that an opportunity to do so was alone waited for, he dared not, however, write to me what my offence really was but that I had incurred the anger of Lopez."

Masterman was placed in a dungeon with a mud floor, the dimensions of which were such that he could neither stand up or lie down. Outside the door a sentry on duty shouted "Sentinela Alerta" every quarter of an hour. "Next to my cell was an open corridor where a great many prisoners were confined in chains which all day clanked dismally. They were of all ages, some very old men, others but boys, but all reduced to the last stage of emaciation, mere brown skin and bone. All had one pair of heavy fetters rivetted on their ankles, rough with callosities and cicatrice of old wounds, several two, and one man bore on his skeleton-like legs three heavy bars,

F

which swung creaking backwards and forwards as he shuffled along."

Masterman was imprisoned in the old Jesuit College, a circumstance that made him write "sometimes when I saw the pale moonlight shining on the wall of the passage and silvering one side of the wide quadrangle, I could catch a glimpse of it through the chink in the window shutter, and the old cloisters beyond half veiled in the black shadows I felt as if I must go mad; the contrast was so painful between the calm beauty of the scene without and the sordid wretchedness within . . . " "One afternoon a poor fellow was estacado, horizontally crucified just beneath my window. Never shall I forget what I endured that day in listening to his moans and occasional frantic yells and prayers for mercy."

Masterman was unable to sleep, the damp affected his health and he was prostrated with fever. It was entirely due to M. Narcisse Lassere, a French distiller in Asuncion, who hearing of Masterman's plight sent him three or four bottles of brandy that he owed his life; and now, if he but knew it, he owed his freedom to Madame Lynch. But of this he was blissfully unaware for he wrote: "I found that I was principally indebted for my liberation to the good offices of the Hon. Charles A. Washburn, United States Minister. He wished me to attend Mrs. Washburn in her approaching accouchment and had applied persistently for my pardon until he obtained it and he now offered me the post of private surgeon to be exchanged for Surgeon to the Legation if the Paraguayan Government should show any intention of molesting me."

If Washburn, on the other hand, had been less gullible he would have been warned by Lopez's bland reply allowing him to avail himself of Masterman's services.

CHAPTER THIRTY-THREE

THE SIEGE OF THE AMERICAN LEGATION

GEORGE FREDERICK MASTERMAN was immediately released from prison and appointed Surgeon to the Legation. No explanation was ever given him why he had been placed in captivity in the first place. He took up his post which carried with it diplomatic immunity, or so he thought, and attended Mrs. Washburn whom he delivered safely of a baby. After the birth of the child time lay heavy on Masterman's hands and he wrote to Senor Sanchez, the Vice-President asking permission to be reinstated in his old post at the hospital. His request was refused on the grounds that he had abstained from serving the Republic and had not attended Mrs. Washburn although he had been liberated by the Marshal-President expressedly for that purpose. Masterman was taken aback by the tone of the letter. Why had the Vice-President written such a deliberate lie? He was stunned by the injustice of the charge and asked Mr. Washburn to supply him with a reference that he might refute the accusation. Washburn immediately went to his desk and wrote out the following testimonial:

G. F. Masterman
Dear Sir,

I reply to your request that I should give you a certificate in regard to your attendance on Mrs. Washburn. I will state you were her sole medical attendant during her illness. I say not only this but that you gave entire satisfaction and that the Vice-President in stating to the contrary must have been misinformed.

Yours faithfully,
Your obedient servant,
Chas. A. Washburn.

Masterman sent the letter to the Vice-President and hopefully awaited a reply. He was unaware that he was the centre of a sinister and complicated plot to involve the American Minister. If Lopez could prove that Washburn had transgressed international law he would be within his rights to arrest him.

In the meantime the American Minister received numerous requests for political asylum from people who had followed his example and had refused to leave the capital. To all who sought a measure of security the American Legation opened its doors. The house was large, occupying an entire block in the Plaza Vieja, the old square, and not unlike a rabbit warren. Rows of windowless rooms opened on to cloistered patios. Among the first to approach Mr. Washburn for protection were Monsieur and Madame Laurent-Cochelet who, being *persona non grata* with Lopez and Madame Lynch, lived in perpetual fear of their lives. Other distinguished personages who sought shelter were don Antonio de la Carrera, former Prime Minister of Montevideo. He had found himself in Paraguay at the commencement of hostilities and had subsequently been prevented from leaving. The Minister was accompanied by Senor Rodriguez, one time Secretary of the Uruguayan Legation. Both these gentlemen were officially enemies of the state. The former was a small, slender man in his early fifties and the latter was a robust young diplomat who for a time had basked in Lopez's favour.

Another who came knocking on the door was Mr. Porter Bliss. He was an American war correspondent, the son of a Baptist Minister, whom Lopez had accused of being a spy. Washburn, with complete lack of tact, made him official translator to the Legation. Besides these personages there were a great number of British merchants and their wives, about forty all told. A few days later they were joined by the Portuguese Consul and his wife. The couple arrived in great distress having been deprived of their diplomatic privileges for helping Brazilian prisoners of war with food and clothing.

Lopez was speechless with rage when he heard that Washburn was openly defying him and harbouring criminals under his roof. Life in the Legation ran far from smoothly. Those who had sought asylum lived in constant fear, not knowing how long Lopez would respect their diplomatic immunity. They were virtually prisoners. Nobody dared venture out into the streets in case they were arrested. Washburn was the one exception who, with true bravado, sallied forth every day and ostentatiously went for a ride through the deserted city. One morning he witnessed a commotion outside the Police station. Mr. Manlove, an English resident, had been detained while taking his cows to water and placed in custody. The Police wanted to know why he had not evacuated the city as ordered. Mr. Manlove, a fiery redhead, was freely using his fists while the guard was trying to hold him down. The Minister came to his rescue, forcibly removed him from the hands of the Police and took him back to the Legation.

It was obvious that Mr. Washburn was not popular with the Authorities. A few days later he was the recipient of a note from don Gumesindo Benitez, the Paraguayan Secretary of State for Foreign Affairs, wanting to know why Senor Leite Pereira was in the Legation without the express consent of His Excellency. To which Mr. Washburn replied that he was not obliged to answer a demand of that kind and that Senor and Senora Leite Pereira were his guests.

The refugees tried to keep up some semblance of normality. The ladies sewed or painted in water colour and the men played billiards and taught themselves languages but tempers were frayed and quarrels were apt to break out on the slightest provocation. Washburn and Manlove fell out over some trifling incident and the Minister told his guest that he was no longer welcome. When Manlove left the house on his dignity, was immediately seized upon by the police and shot, the representative of the United States was beside himself with remorse.

To add to their difficulties they suffered an epidemic of Asiatic cholera. Hardly any one escaped the illness from the

Minister to Basilio, the negro porter. Masterman was kept busy going from one bed of sickness to another. Then, food was becoming increasingly difficult to obtain. It seemed that their only hope lay in the quick relief of Asuncion by the Allies. But with their usual lethargy the combined forces took their time in following up their initial gains. Washburn, as soon as he had recovered sufficiently from the attack of cholera, spent his days scanning the approaches to the harbour with a telescope.

He could hardly believe his eyes when, finally, he saw two Brazilian monitors steaming up the river. "Masterman. Masterman. Come at once," he called.

Masterman ran to do his bidding and focused the lenses. True enough they were saved. People came running from all directions talking excitedly. Madame Laurent-Cochelet clapped her hands and repeated like a child "Ils sont venus".

The household were elated and felt that their troubles were over. Merciful Heavens. They had been rescued from the clutches of the madman.

To get a better view of the battleships, Mr. Washburn, M. Laurent-Cochelet and Masterman climbed on to the roof of the Legation. They fully expected the ironclads to land their troops and take possession of the town. To their astonishment the Monitors opened up their broadsides and bombarded the undefended capital. The few remaining inhabitants fled to the outlying villages. The front of a house fell exposing a family. The great dome of the Presidential palace was struck and collapsed with a roar, shaking the city like an earthquake, and a couple of dogs were blown to pieces in the market square.

After four hours of continuous firing the ironclads returned down the river as unexpectedly as they had come. The feeling of elation turned to despair. They had come so near to freedom that their disappointment was the more acute.

Until quite late that evening they stood about in groups speculating on their chances of escape. Suddenly they heard the eery clanging of a bell. They looked at each other. Who could it be at this time of the night? Those who had taken shelter felt both guilty and trapped. Basilio unbolted the door and, to their utter amazement, Madame Lynch walked into the courtyard followed by forty emancipated slaves carrying boxes on their heads. Those who had never seen her, and there were many among the refugees to whom she was merely a legendary figure, were struck by her amazing beauty. She was wearing a brown hood and cloak over a grey dress which somehow gave her the look of a novice. Her Irish complexion glowed like that of a young girl of eighteen and her eyes were as grey and misty as the skies of her own country. There was not a man present who did not uncover his head at the sight of Madame Lynch.

The American Minister cleared his throat and strode forward to receive her.

"Mr. Washburn," she said, "May I place the public treasure of Paraguay as well as my own personal property in your safe keeping?"

Mr. Washburn was clearly taken aback by the request but answered civilly, "They will be placed with the other valuables entrusted to my care."

Earlier that day, as soon as the news had reached headquarters by bush telegraph that the Brazilians were about to land in Asuncion, Eliza had volunteered to ride into the city to prevent the gold reserves from falling into the hands of the Macacos.

"Where are you going to hide it?" Lopez had asked.

"In the vaults of the American Legation."

Lopez laughed until the tears ran down his face. "No one can accuse you of not being resourceful."

"There is nothing like making use of our enemies," she had replied with an angelic expression.

Neither of them had any scruples about taking advantage of a man they both despised and whose downfall they were plotting if by so doing they could save the public funds.

Eliza set off on horseback with a mounted guard and slaves that ran before her horse like a pack of hounds with their tongues hanging out of their mouths. It took her seven hours to complete the journey from San Fernando to Asuncion. With her own hands she unlocked the doors of the cellars where the gold was kept and supervised the withdrawal of the bullion.

Eliza went out of her way to be charming to Mr. Washburn. As soon as she had seen the gold safely deposited in the Legation she retired. The Minister escorted her as far as the outer gate. She thanked him kindly and gave him her hand to kiss and then, like a Queen, dropped a half curtsey with a slight mocking gesture.

A few days later, as soon as the immediate danger of a Brazilian invasion was past, Madame Lynch returned for her property. The same slaves who had brought the boxes now took them away and loaded them on to oxen carts. Whereas on the previous occasion Madame Lynch had been gracious, this time she was distant and cold. Most pointedly she turned round to Mr. Washburn and said, "I suppose you know that a great conspiracy has been discovered."

When the Minister did not reply, she continued, "It is incredible that any one could be so wicked as to conspire against the President."

After a further pause in which she allowed the context to sink into his confused mind, she continued, "Berges swears that the papers were deposited with you." She fixed him with eyes as hard as steel. Washburn flushed with anger and embarrassment. "You ought to give them up and trust to the mercy of the President," she said in a tone of acrid sweetness. "He takes pleasure in pardoning penitent offenders."

After another pause she turned on her heels and left. Mrs. Washburn, who was an impulsive little woman ran after her and clasping both her hands said with tears in her eyes, "I beg of you to use your influence and persuade the President to think kindly of my husband."

According to Mrs. Washburn's testimonial some months later in Washington, Eliza Lynch had answered, "That remains to be seen."

Washburn was left with an uneasy feeling. It was the first time that an admission of a plot against the President had been stated although there had been plenty of rumours to that effect. Then Madame Lynch had referred to the letters of Berges. What letters? He was frankly perplexed.

He was a good deal more distressed when he received a letter from don Gumesindo Benitez asking him to return a packet of letters that had been left with him by don José Berges the ex-Minister of Foreign Affairs who had confessed to being implicated in the conspiracy and was now a prisoner at San Fernando. Mr. Washburn was too blunt and honest an individual to realize the Machiavellian trap that Lopez and Madame Lynch were laying for him. He wrote back denying categorically that he knew anything of the existence of these letters.

The demand was subsequently repeated and with it came a note from Berges written in a trembling hand, "My treason being now discovered, concealment is now useless, therefore I beg of you, Mr. Washburn, to give up the two letters marked 'Papeles de Berges' which I confided to you." With diabolical cunning, Berges went on to describe the last interview that was supposed to have taken place between them at don Benigno's house on the evening of March 2nd. "You cannot have forgotten, Mr. Washburn, that I accompanied you back to the Legation. You took the papers out of a red despatch box and deposited them in an iron safe that stands in a corner of your study."

The irony of the situation was that Mr. Washburn had actually seen Berges on the date mentioned and although he had not been carrying a despatch case on that particular night, the one alluded to tallied with the portfolio he had taken to the house of the Senora Presidenta on the occasion of their last meeting.

The American Minister was being drawn more and more into the snare that Lopez and Madame Lynch were preparing for him. He was involved in a series of half truths. He could not deny having seen Berges on the date mentioned, he could not deny posessing a red despatch case, he could not deny having a safe in the corner of his office and he could not deny having called on the Senora Presidenta on the day that the plot was supposed to have been hatched.

Mr. Washburn's hopes were raised again when he saw a gunboat coming up the river. He prayed that she might be an American line of battleship but she turned out to be a French frigate come to rescue the Laurent-Cochelets. For fear of reprisal, Lopez was obliged to give them their passports but kept the ship in quarantine for a week hoping that a stray bomb might finish them off. This was the sort of situation that appealed to Lopez's sense of humour and he laughed heartily at "el gran susto que pasaron" "the big fright they received."

Although Washburn tried to hide his disappointment, he was exceedingly upset to think that the French had escaped while the Americans had been left in the wilderness. Those that had taken shelter in the Legation resumed their precarious lives. Like all people living under nervous strain their moods alternated between deep anxiety and unaccountable hilarity that made Lopez accuse them of orgies. Each time there was a knock at the outer gate their hearts sank. What new portentious tidings? How much longer would Lopez respect their neutrality? After an interval of more nerveracking days, another long despatch was received from Benitez demanding the immediate expulsion of Doctor de la Carrera and Senor Rodriguez. They were both accused of being involved in the conspiracy to overthrow the Regime. Washburn was warned that any refusal to hand over the prisoners would be regarded as lèse majesté. To this last intimidating letter Washburn replied bluntly that as long as these gentlemen wished to remain under the protection of the American flag they were welcome to stay at the Legation. But the Uruguayan diplomats realized that they were imposing on the Minister's kindness and jeopardizing his life and, although they were fully conscious of the danger awaiting them, they felt they could no longer remain an

obligation to him. Mr. Washburn was torn between his
honour as an American gentleman and the safety of his
family. The nervous tension was undermining his strength
and he was becoming increasingly irritable. Therefore when
de la Carrera and Rodriguez decided to go rather than continue to embarrass him, he made no effort to stop them. The
ex-diplomats said goodbye gravely and left the Legation with
drawn faces and dark rings under their eyes. No sooner had
they passed the porte-cochere than they were seized upon by
the police, who had been watching for that purpose and
escorted to San Fernando.

As a protest of Washburn's treatment of de la Carrera and
Rodriguez the English merchants decided to leave in a body,
feeling that they could no longer inflict their presence on the
Minister. They were immediately taken into custody and
more than one was shot.

Three days after the departure of de la Carrera, his written
confession was handed in at the door. It was accompanied by
two affidavits one signed by Berges and the other bearing
the signature of Captain Fidanza, an Italian sea Captain
whose ship had been seized by Lopez, all testifying to their
share in the conspiracy. They implored Washburn to acknowledge that he was the principal instigator and, each in turn,
reminded him of a large sum of money that don Benigno had
given him to distribute among them and of which they
were in need. Once again Washburn was compromised because it was true that don Benigno had entrusted him with
a quantity of gold—his own personal fortune. All the letters
were so cleverly written that they were difficult to refute.
Instead of ignoring these declarations, obviously written
under pressure, Washburn replied to each of them separately,
thinking to prove his innocence but naively implicating himself the more. He was no match for the pair in power. With
nerveracking regularity, every ten days or so, a voluminous
despatch arrived from the Minister of Foreign Affairs, always
worded in the most polite language, imploring Mr. Washburn to admit his guilt. Far from veiling his replies in dip-

lomatic language, Washburn invariably answered in the most insulting manner. Lopez retaliated by publishing the whole of the correspondence in the *Semanario* which, if it did not actually prove the American's guilt, at least made him look ridiculous.

The over-sensitive ears of those harboured in the Legation were disturbed by ominous footsteps. There was a pause, prior to a knock. But instead of the usual letter, don Gumesindo Benitez, the Minister of Foreign Affairs appeared in person. He was sleek and had a good opinion of himself. Don Gumesindo was shown into Mr. Washburn's study and greeted his host with exaggerated politeness and recited a speech which he had prepared beforehand and then pointing to the safe he begged Washburn to give up the incriminating papers. "I implore you to supply the conclusive evidence and spare the Government from resorting to extremes." This was tantamount to a threat.

"The Government can take whatever course it sees fit. As for me I have nothing more to say on the matter." White with rage, he stood up to show that the interview was at an end.

Don Gumesindo pleaded in a whining voice, "Why go on pretending? Sabemos todo. All is discovered. You must confess."

Unfortunately Mr. Washburn lost his temper and showed his visitor to the door.

The Minister of Foreign Affairs despite his cold reception followed up his visit with a letter in which he repeated the words, "All is discovered. You must confess," and then wrote, "Did you not inform us that the conspiracy was planned to break out on the birthday of the President?" This was a trap and Washburn fell right into it by declaring, "I never told you that the conspiracy was planned to break out on the President's birthday."

Whereupon Benitez quickly retaliated by saying, "It was not I, Senor Ministro, who spoke of the revolution breaking out the day you have mentioned, but I thank you for the information."

Washburn was furious that his words had been twisted and for days he went round the house stamping his feet and mumbling to himself. "No fui yo Senor Ministro."

However it was the last letter that Benitez was to write because Lopez, suspecting everybody, decided that he would not have used the affirmative statement *"All is discovered. You must confess"* if he himself had not been involved in the conspiracy and promptly threw him into prison.

The arrest of Mr. Washburn was expected hourly. The American Legation was surrounded by pickets and a chain of sentries that kept closing in step by step. It was only the timely arrival of the U.S. Wasp that saved the situation. After considerable pressure from the gunboat, Lopez allowed him to depart on condition that he gave up Senor and Senora Leite Pereira and the "criminals" Bliss and Masterman. Both these men, although technically one had British nationality, were officially members of the Legation and should have been allowed to leave with the rest of the staff but Washburn was so relieved at finding deliverance within his grasp that, despite his strongest protests, he sacrificed them for his own personal freedom.

For fear of last minute reprisals it was arranged that Mrs. Washburn, Katie, her maid, the first Secretary Mr. Mielcke and two English servants should leave the Legation in advance of Mr. Washburn. Once they were safely on board the Wasp, it was agreed that a rocket would be fired in the air as a signal for the Minister to embark.

For all of them it was a restless night. The cloisters sighed with the equinoxial winds and the dismal rooms resounded with the heartbreaking sobs of Senora Leite Pereira. Masterman spent the sleepless hours writing farewell letters to his family. At dawn they had a frugal breakfast of milk and ship's biscuits. Not long after, the Italian Consul and the Acting French Consul, M. de Libertad, who had replaced M. Laurent-Cochelet, arrived to bid the Americans godspeed.

Mr. Washburn entrusted them with the valuables that had been left in his care. These included a quantity of silver plate, jewels and golden coins, all of which fell into Lopez's hands the minute Washburn had departed. Trunks and stores were carried on board ship and Mrs. Washburn and her party departed after many tearful farewells and not without misgivings.

At last a salvo was heard that meant freedom for some and perhaps death for others. Mr. Washburn said goodbye all round and shook everybody by the hand. When he came to Bliss and Masterman he repeated, "Once I have gone you can accuse me of any crime you like if by so doing you can obtain your own freedom." At a sign from the American Minister the double gates of the porte-cochère were flung open and all those who had sheltered in the Legation for five months marched out in a body with a sinking feeling in the pit of the stomach. Mr. Washburn led the way walking fast with his head in the air. Masterman says that he never looked round although he might have offered some protection. The moment they emerged in the street the police ran forward drawing their swords and arrested Senor and Senora Leite Pereira as well as Bliss and Masterman. The two last mentioned were seized upon by thirty armed guards, taken to the police station and thrown into a cell.

Despite the fact that Lopez had been unable to lay his hands on Washburn, he had made certain to secure two witnesses, one English and one American, to testify that Washburn had been the chief conspirator in the plot to overthrow him.

CHAPTER THIRTY-FOUR

BLOOD JUDGES

LOPEZ decided to abandon his position at San Fernando and withdrew to La Villeta, forty leagues up the river. To cover his hasty retreat he left Colonel Thompson with a scanty garrison at Angostura (the Narrows) which occupied a strategic position along the river and was the last fortress still in Paraguayan hands.

But La Villeta was untenable because of a sudden thrust by the Brazilians who circumvented the river and unexpectedly cut across the Chaco, thus obliging Lopez to fall back on Lomas Valentinas.

The Marshal seldom accompanied the army on the march but went ahead with a few picked men and his personal bodyguard, to choose a suitable site in which to set up a camp. Behind the President drove Madame Lynch and her children in an old Spanish carriage with high wheels and leather springs. Carts followed in their wake containing the Treasury of Paraguay and the jewelry that had been seized from the people. The starving multitudes, old men, hags, children and prisoners in chains brought up the rear. Among the prisoners were Generals, officers, soldiers, priests and countless women including his own mother and sisters who lived in a covered wagon. The people had become mere skeletons; their skin had assumed the transparency of parchment and only their eyes gleamed with fever.

Not since Biblical days had one man driven an entire nation into the wilderness. They sustained themselves on roots, grass and the barks of trees. The wild oranges in the groves proved to be deceptive, bitter and inedible. Apart from the civilian population that accompanied him, he still had an army of thirteen thousand men but of these only three thousand were serviceable troops, the rest were mere boys and crippled veterans. His baggage animals were skeletons and the cavalry could hardly raise a trot.

In spite of the overwhelming obstacles, Lopez repulsed at Lomas Valentinas an attack from the enemy so effectively that he was able to entrench himself for several months. Long enough, in fact, to establish a Criminal Court. He ordered don Francisco Saguier, an eminent Judge from Asuncion, to set up a tribunal to try the conspirators, including his own family, for their supposed share in the plot.

Don Francisco Saguier, an honest and conscientious man undertook the thankless task; but he could find no evidence of guilt and the prisoners were acquitted. Lopez was beside himself with rage. "You should have made them confess under torture," he shouted at the conscientious Judge. "Traitors that they are." Saguier was promptly arrested, loaded with irons and exposed to the sun for five months. Between June and December 1869 Lopez had more than six hundred victims put to death. At one moment he contemplated mass suicide, at the next he felt predestined to lead Paraguay. His mission, in his eyes, was holy and the ignorant Guarani followed him as though he were a god. They were a brave race, but docile and irresponsible, exhausting his patience to the limits of endurance and driving him through sheer desperation to commit excesses. He went to the extent of ordering that Mongeles, the head of his personal body guard, should be put to death. "I know you to be innocent" he said, "but a person in your position had no right to be unaware of a conspiracy against me and because of that I am having you shot."

As if to compensate for the miscarriage of justice, the blood he spilt and the tortures inflicted in his name, he was seized with religious mania and spent long hours on his knees at an octagonal chapel standing near the house he had commandeered. When he was not at prayer he would assist at sexual orgies, making men and women fornicate before his eyes and devising ever more exotic perversions for them to perform before him.

Madame Lynch held aloof from this side of his nature but she was not above procuring him a girl or two or even young boys if they caught his fancy.

Masterman and Bliss, weighed down with fetters rivetted to their ankles, were bodily lifted on to pack mules and made to ride pillion for a distance of thirty five miles. Masterman begged his jailor to lead the animal as slowly as possible because the jolting was agonizing to an extreme. The man kind-heartedly complied but, going down a hill, the mule broke into a trot and Masterman was thrown and dragged some distance by the kicking animal.

They rode through a countryside of utter desolation. An earth that was scorched by the sun and turned into swamps by the rains. Withered orange trees and abandoned quintas lay along their path. From a hill-top Masterman could see with feverish eyes, the lights of a steamer in the river. It was the Wasp carrying Mr. Washburn to safety.

Shaken, bruised and blistered, they arrived at headquarters. On being untied from their mules the prisoners fell exhausted on the ground. A cadet ordered Masterman to stand up. In his book, "Seven years in Paraguay" Masterman writes, "I tried but the weight of my irons threw me on my face. Go faster, he shouted and thrashed me savagely with his stick".

Masterman was taken before Captain Falcon who sat in a hut with an evil-looking priest "Ah, we've got you at last," he said. "Now confess that Washburn was the chief conspirator and that you took refuge in the Legation for the purpose of plotting against the Government." When Masterman failed to answer he was put in the "potro"—the rack—and the priest bent over him menacingly. "You will not confess?" "I have nothing to confess. I am innocent." Whereupon the priest nodded his head and two soldiers brought out a bundle of muskets, and ropes of hide.

"One of the men tied my arms tightly behind me, the other passed a musket under my knees, and then putting his foot between my shoulders forced my head down until my throat rested on the lower musket, a second was put over the back of my neck and they were firmly lashed together. The priest meanwhile in a monotonous voice, as if he were repeating a formula, urged me to confess and receive the mercy of the kind and generous Marshal Lopez. I made no reply but suffered the intense pain they were inflicting in silence. First the feet went to sleep, then a tingling commenced in the toes, gradually extending to the knees. My tongue swelled up and I thought my jaw would have been displaced. I lost all feeling on one side of my face. At length they unbound me and I was asked once more, "Will you confess?" I could not answer. They bound me up as before, but with two muskets at the back of my neck."

Mr. Alonzo Taylor, the master builder of Lopez's palace in Asuncion who suffered a similar fate describes this torture —the *Uruguayana*—as a thousand times worse than all the devices of Torquemada.

The next time that Masterman was brought before the blood Judges, as the inquisitors were called, he thought it more prudent to exclaim "I am guilty. I will confess," and he tried to remember all the indiscreet things that Washburn had said about Lopez and blurted out names at random such as Carrera, Berges, Benigno Lopez, in fact any one who came into his head.

A priest sneered at these unconvincing revelations and begged Captain Falcon to put him back in the *Uruguayana* and make an end of him. At night they were joined by another priest, named Roman. He was unshaven and had a mean and crafty look. "Que miserables disparates." What rot!" he exclaimed on reading over the false testimony. "Now look you. I go for a short ride and if on my return I do not find that you have confessed clearly, I will put you in the *Uruguayana* and keep you there until you do."

The blood judges, sinister and inquisitional, sat behind a table with a broken leg. Masterman faced them seated on a low stool. A solitary candle burned in a saucer. Two sentinels kept guard outside the hut. "Come, Masterman," said his tormentor, not unkindly, "Confess that the great beast (gran bestia) Washburn was the chief conspirator, that he was in treaty with Caxias, that he received money and letters from the enemy and that you knew it." Falcon who was short, stout and bald and wore silver rimmed spectacles, found it easier to use his imagination than to listen to Masterman's incoherent words. He went on writing for some time. Suddenly he looked up and asked "How much were you offered?" "Not a real". "Senor, Capitan," interrupted the priest, "Put this anaru, this son of a bitch in the potro. He is misleading us with lies."

"No. No." Masterman stammered. "I was only told part of the plan because Washburn feared I might denounce him." This statement seemed to satisfy Falcon who listened with evident approval and proceeded to put pen to paper. The scratching of a quill went on for some time. He read back what he had written. "I admit I am guilty of conspiring against His Excellency and I throw myself at the mercy of the Marshal-President." After an hour or so Masterman was told that he could get down from his stool and was allowed to return to the patio. "I wrapped my poncho around me and I fell asleep. When I awoke in the morning I found I was lying in a pool of water (heavy rain had fallen and the wind was bitterly cold). On one side of me, bound, was don Carlos de la Carrera still sleeping and the corpse of Lieutenant-Colonel Campos on the other. The latter had died during the night and lay there staring blankly with open eyes at the rising sun. As soon as de la Carrera awoke, the man, who had been Prime Minister of his country for twelve years and Ambassador in London started scavenging among the prisoners' refuse and picking the gristles of the bones." Further along Masterman saw a row of priests in chains and naked men exposed to the elements on an ant hill. His narrative continues; "From one of the hovels near me crept out on all fours don Benigno Lopez, the President's brother; he was well dressed but heavily ironed; and from another, a spectral old man whom I was long in recognizing as the ex-Minister for Foreign Affairs, don Jose Berges. He was leaning feebly on a hedge stake, and was followed by his successor don Gumesindo Benitez, bareheaded and with naked fettered feet."

CHAPTER THIRTY-FIVE

REGIMENT OF AMAZONS

ONCE again Lopez gave the orders to retreat to the north-East The prisoners were herded together and driven forwards over hills, swamps and valleys like cattle, prodded by guards with fixed bayonets. Two old men, too weak to walk, were lifted on to a litter made of hide and carried by soldiers. They looked around with timid smiles, evidently unconscious of what was going on.

Masterman's companions on the march were Leite Pereira, Captain Fidanza, Berges, don Benigno, don Venancio, Benitez and la Carrera with whom he carried on a whispered conversation.

"Is there any truth in the conspiracy?"

"No. No . All lies from the beginning to end. Has Mr. Washburn gone?"

"Yes. He is out of the country."

"Have you confessed?"

"Yes."

"You have done well. That terrible Father Maiz tortured me with the *Uruguayana* on three successive occasions and then smashed my fingers with a mallet."

In sheer exhaustion the prisoners collapsed everytime they stopped by the wayside. They were either drenched to the skin by the tropical rain or exposed to the broiling sun. Their lips were cracked and their tongues were dry and leathery. "Agua. Por Amor de Dinos. Agua," they pleaded. Fettered, they stumbled over volcanic stones or wallowed in marshy ground. The spectacle was like Dante's Inferno. Heavy blows, dull thuds and quick incisive lashes resounded on all sides.

One day they were overtaken by a carriage and pair in which sat Marshal Lopez and Madame Lynch. Masterman says "She bowed with a gracious smile; we took off our caps to her all well knowing that a word from her could send us to the scaffold, or worse, on the morrow." They overheard her say, "Oh, Your Excellency, how you have sacrificed yourself for the sake of your country and these wicked men have conspired against you. Es muy triste, Senor. Oh very sad indeed."

The troops, the stragglers and the prisoners arrived at Pykisyri, formerly a Jesuit Capilla, now a collection of mean huts by the side of a dried river bed. Here Lopez set up a provisional capital and as usual commandeered the best house for himself and Madame Lynch. He remained long enough to cast several guns. Bands played continually to bolster the flagging spirits of his pitiful army. The few survivors after the war could never again bear to hear the strains of "La Palomita", Lopez's favourite Habanera without it bringing back memories of lashings, lynchings and the dreaded *Uruguayana*.

On September 23rd, 1868, don Benigno Lopez was put to the torture. He was taken away in the early morning and did not return till late in the afternoon. He crept on all fours with his face contorted in pain. On September 24th don Cumesindo Benitez was led out of the camp. He did not return. The words "All is discovered. You must confess" were his own death sentence. On the 27th of the same month a guard with fixed bayonets, came and fetched Doctor de la Carrera and Captain Alen, the latter horribly mutilated. A couple of priests and a squad of men with spades accompanied them.

On a day that the firing was particularly heavy the Sentry asked a Sergeant "Are those the Cambas?"

"No" said the Sergeant calmly. "They are only shooting the presos" (the prisoners).

Masterman was called before Father Maiz. The Chief Inquisitor waited for him alone by the stump of a tree. The Jesuit was an ascetic-looking man who might have stepped down from a canvas by El Greco. He had salved his own conscience by convincing himself that the tortures of the flesh were no small price to pay for the salvation of a soul and he was hopeful that he might be recompensed in Heaven for his campaign on earth.

"Why, Masterman, your hair is quite grey."

"That is not surprising since I have been in prison for eleven months."

Far from submitting him to any further punishment, Father Maiz informed him that the President had commuted his sentence of death to banishment for life and trusted, to use his own words, "That I would employ the rest of my days in praising the clemency of the Marshal."

The English Apothecary was overcome with relief. He was unaware that a new Minister from the United States had arrived and had made it a condition that before presenting his credentials the two members of the Legation who had been forcibly detained, i.e. Masterman and Bliss, should be released. Lopez had very clearly replied "I personally had been in favour of releasing them all along but have been prevented from doing so by the Tribunales. However I am willing to waive aside the course of justice if they swear their written depositions before a naval court composed of officers of the U.S. Wasp." It was the same ship that had taken Mr. Washburn to safety which had now brought the new American Minister to Paraguay and on which the prisoners were being deported. Masterman says "I bitterly resented having to do such a thing but was convinced that they were aware of my innocence." To his surprise he was treated like a common criminal on board ship and it was only when he got to Washington that he was able to prove his innocence. Had Lopez foreseen that Masterman was to write "Seven Years in Paraguay" he would never have been allowed to leave the country.

From the moment that General MacMahon, one of the heroes of the American civil war, presented his credentials to the Marshal-President he proved as popular with Lopez and Madame Lynch as his predecessor Washburn had been detested. At his first official reception he handed Lopez a flag dedicated to Santo Tomas, the patron Saint of Paraguay. Both Francisco and Eliza pretended to take him into their confidence and invited him to stay at headquarters. They assured him that the Allies would retreat in time and sue for peace. The American General was mesmerized by Lopez and spell-bound by Madame Lynch. On those evenings that they did not play whist with Colonel Wisner, they sat smoking on the verandah and, according to Doctor Stewart, drinking excellent claret. The Scotsman declared "that even in this backwater Madame Lynch's house exuded an air of Europe." Lopez puffed at his cigar and accused Washburn of infringing International law. "I have the positive proof that he was the chief conspirator in the plot to overthrow me. He should be brought to trial." MacMahon promised to submit a detailed report to Washington and assured the President that proceedings would be instituted against Mr. Washburn by the State Department.

On December 21st, 1869, the camp was submitted to a tremendous bombardment by a combined force of Brazilians and Argentines that numbered twenty five thousand men commanded by Marshal Caxias. Lopez abandoned his temporary quarters and erected a tent about a mile to the rear among the woods at Pikysiry, from where he conducted operations, but left the American Minister, to whom he entrusted his sons, in the comparative safety of Pirebebuy. Madame Lynch insisted on accompanying the Marshal.

Suddenly all was confusion. The Brazilians were upon them. "Los Macacos. Los Macacos," shouted the surprised troops, running in all directions.

Bullets hissed through the air. Intermittent firing and the heavier boom of guns shook the earth. Lopez, afraid of being taken prisoner, ran and sheltered in the stunted undergrowth. Black faces seemed to emerge from every side. Close by, in a corral, stood a team of two hundred cadaverous horses that had been captured from the enemy two days previously. Eliza looked around her. There was not a man in sight. Then her eyes fell on a group of semi-naked Guarani women, the destinadas, part of that army that she had raised, keeping guard over a heap of muskets and lances stacked in pyramids. "To arms," she shouted. "Untie the horses. Attack." Each woman, following the example of their leader, took a lance and with a leap mounted an emaciated animal. "Trot. Gallop. Charge." commanded the clear voice of Eliza Lynch as she led a cavalry charge. The women dug their bare heels into those starving beasts frenzied with heat, thirst and hunger, and sprang forward like leaping flames before they fizzle out. "Faster. Faster," shouted Eliza. On came the women of Paraguay. Bent forwards, riding bareback, carrying their lances under their armpits and managing their horses with a bare rope, they stormed the enemy ranks. "Death to the Cambas. Forward." Eliza's golden hair streamed behind her in the wind.

The Brazilians seeing a horde of wild women coming towards them like a tidal wave turned tail and fled. In the instant that the Regiment of Amazons had won the day and were following up their gains, Eliza's horse stumbled. The beast trembled, pranced on its hind legs, and fell like a log. Eliza lay motionless, white as marble, pinned to the ground beneath the weight of the dead animal whose lungs had burst with the supreme effort of obeying its rider. Eliza was rescued by Colonel von Wisner who had witnessed the scene from afar and came running to her aid. The Hungarian officer, with the help of six men, lifted the animal and gently withdrew the bruised and bleeding form of the heroine of the day. She was placed on a crude litter and carried back to the tent. Everyone feared the worst, and even more, the wrath of Lopez.

The Marshal sensed that something was wrong and came stumping out of the woods. When Francisco saw Eliza he stopped dead in his tracks, and his pupils dilated; at the same moment, she opened her eyes and endeavoured to smile.

The look of relief on Lopez's face was touching in its intensity. Then he turned on her in fury, "How dare you expose your life you wilful stupid woman. I forbid you. Nay. I command you never again to lay yourself open to an attack. My life may be necessary to lead my people to victory but yours is necessary to me."

This time Eliza opened wide her eyes. Francisco was beside himself with rage but never had he spoken words to her of such extreme tenderness.

CHAPTER THIRTY-SIX

ULTIMATUM

On Christmas day 1868 all was quiet. Then a group of Brazilian officers presented themselves at Lopez's headquarters under the flag of truce and handed him a written intimation. He read it through to the end, tore the paper in strips and trampled the pieces underfoot.

Never would they make him surrender.

Seated on a stool and using the stump of a tree as a desk he wrote the following reply:

"To their Excellencies, Marshall the Marques de Caxias, Colonel-Major Don Enrique Castro and Brigadier General Don Juan A Gelly y Obes.

The Marshal-President of the Republic of Paraguay ought perhaps to decline sending a written answer to their Excellencies the Generals in Chief of the Allied Army, in war against the nation he presides over, on account of the unusual tone and language of their demand.

Your Excellencies have thought proper to send me an intimation to lay down my arms within a term of twelve hours and make me responsible to my country, to the nations which your excellencies represent, and to the civilized world for the blood spilled and yet to be spilled if I do not obey the order.

For my part I am prepared to negotiate a just termination of the war upon a basis equally honourable for all belligerents concerned but I am not disposed to listen to an intimation to lay down my arms.

If blood is still to flow the responsibility will be on those who prolong the struggle.

My Generals, Chiefs, Officers and troops to whom I have communicated Your Excellencies intimation are in complete harmony with my sentiments. In writing Your Excellencies to treat of peace therefore I consider that I am, in my turn, fulfilling an imperative duty towards religion, humanity and civilization as well as to which I owe my own name.

Francisco Solano Lopez.

God preserve Your Excellencies many years.

In this way the Marshal turned the tables on the Allies and made them responsible for the continuance of the massacre. The year ended disastrously for Lopez with the surrender of Angostura by Colonel Thompson. The loss to the President of his one remaining fort meant that the entire stretch of the Paraguay was open to the Allies. From now onwards Lopez and his miserable army became a wandering tribe of nomads.

General MacMahon, the American Minister, remained five months at Lopez's headquarters and was then recalled to Washington. Both Lopez and Eliza were genuinely sorry to see him go. His presence gave them a sense of security. They felt that as long as he was among them they had a powerful ally in the person of the representative of the United States. MacMahon promised that on his return to North America he would do all in his power to swing public opinion in their favour and assured them that if he could not get Congress to come to their aid he would raise an army of volunteers.

Cecilio Baez, the historian and Paraguayan Minister in Washington who was no friend of Lavinche, asserts that she had completely captivated the American Minister and that she took advantage of his departure on the Wasp to send out of the country a quantity of boxes which contained the gold and jewelry extracted from the women of Paraguay. Baez states that the money was weighed "onza por onza y Carlos

IV" por Carlos,* in the counting house of Pirebebuy under the supervision of the Chief of Police, don Manuel Solalinda.

Before leaving the country Lopez entrusted General Mac-Mahon with a copy of his will and asked him to be his executor.

General MacMahon was genuinely sorry to see the last of this beleagured little country and bid farewell to his friends the Marshal-President and Madame Lynch, "one of the most bewitching and gallant ladies it has ever been my privilege to meet," as he expressed himself later in the United States. Once on board ship he took out of his pocket the document that had been entrusted to his safe-keeping and read the following:

Dear Sir,

As a precaution against any unforeseen contingency that may prevent me from seeing you again, I permit myself the liberty to place in your care the enclosed deed of gift by which I transfer to Madame Eliza Lynch all my goods and properties of whatever nature. I beg you as a representative of a friendly nation to have the goodness to keep that document in your possession until you can either return it to me or deliver safely to the said lady.

I also avail myself of this opportunity to beg of you to carry into effect the dispositions made in the said documents.

Thanking you in anticipation for all you may do.

Your very obedient servant
Francisco S. Lopez.

Enclosed with this letter was a copy of the Marshal's will.

I, the undersigned President of the Republic of Paraguay, by this document, declare formally and solemnly that thankful for the services of Madame Eliza Lynch, I make in her favour a prime and perfect gift of all my goods,

*Obsolete Spanish coins.

rights and personal effects and it is my wish that this disposition be faithfully and legally complied with.

Signed in the presence of witnesses at my head-quarters of Piksyry on 23rd December, 1868.

Lopez had made his will on the date of Eliza's near-fatal accident.

CHAPTER THIRTY-SEVEN

SAINT CHRISTIAN LOPEZ

AT night the Indian drum La Gomba sounded in monotonous smouldering rhythm from the encampment where the half starved soldiers huddled around the smouldering fires.

Up until now Lopez had kept up a veneer of civilization but here, in the depth of the forest, he reverted to his ancestors. He was the all powerful *Carai Guzu*. From Pirebebuy, Lopez was forced to fall back on a place called Oscura. It has often been stressed that after the battle of Pirebebuy Solano Lopez gave the orders for the Treasury of Paraguay to be hidden, rather than it should fall into the hands of the Brazilians. Emaciated men, loaded like pack animals, climbed to the summit of the mbaracayo and threw the gold over the cliff. Countless legends have been woven but no one lived to tell the tale because Solano Lopez ordered that these men should follow suit and hurl themselves over the cliff to guard the treasure in perpetuity. Since then, expeditions have set out and explorers have endeavoured to retrieve the hidden gold but so far all attempts have failed and the secret of Solano Lopez has been kept.

The War had resolved itself into a death struggle between Lopez and the Brazilians. The Uruguayan forces had long since gone home and the Argentines were exhausted by the long struggle. The Emperor of Brazil, hoping to make a quick decisive end to the conflict, had recalled Marshal Caxias and had given the surpreme command to his son-in-law, the Comte d'Eu.

From Oscura Lopez retired to Curuguaytay, which was no more than a collection of reed huts. Virgin forests and unexplored mountains stretched to the North and to the East.

Tigers, pumas, wild boars and tapirs roamed at large and an occasional Carrigua Indian armed with a blow pipe would suddenly appear and as mysteriously withdraw.

In a corral surrounded by six hundred bullock carts, a camp altar was erected and Lopez was the centre of a bizzare ceremony. Francisco Solano may not have achieved his ambition of having himself crowned Emperor of South America but he surpassed himself when the Sacred College of Paraguay, instigated by Father Maiz, elected to make him a Saint of the Christian Church. All who did not vote unaminously were shot. They were but twenty three victims.

Rows of black hooded priests, perspiring in the tropical night intoned the Magnificat. Francisco stood before the altar looking like a bull and was anointed, glorified, beatified and sanctified. Six hundred voices burst into song and chanted Gloria in Excelsis. Costly robes were clasped around the Marshal's shoulders and on his head was placed a Bishop's mitre which was later discarded for a gold biretta. Furthermore, Father Maiz announced that the date of Francisco's birth would be set aside in the Christian calendar as the Saint's day of the new Apostolate of God.

To Eliza Lynch the blasphemous ritual had no more significance than the ceremony of washing the feet of the poor on Maunday Thursday.

To herself she sang a song of hate. She could not visualize a God that could allow such pain far less a God of Love. It seemed to her that God was a destructive force that took away the moment that it gave; a ruthless, terrible avalanche that uprooted all before it. How could any God of sensitivity allow such cruelty to be committed in his name. Surely he would avert his eyes and weep or had he turned to stone as she had done? It was obvious that, to nature, humanity was of no importance and man, Francisco or any other, irresponsible for his actions. He was part of a cosmic force that had as much will as the elements. She could see no proof of God's existence, only a denial, a sorry pretence at light by the dark forces of nature. What were the sufferings of Christ compared with the suffering of man? Was not each man crucified in his own life here. Eliza realized that she had not the brains to grasp the truth she sought. Only of this, could she be certain, man was powerless in the grip of destiny and all destiny drove man to destruction.

Once Francisco Solano had received the homage due to his new Saintliness, he ordered a secret conclave and had his mother brought to trial before an Ecclesiastical court. She was found guilty of treason to the Holy Ruler. Despite her seventy years, her back was bared, her hands were tied to a cross and with the utmost indignity she was flogged before a body of priests. Although she was his mother, Francisco would show no mercy. All, all who conspired against the State must be treated alike. Then the venerable old lady was made to place one hand on the altar and swear, "I recognise Francisco Solano, alone of all my children, as my legitimate offspring, the rest are mere traitors and bastards," she repeated and fainted.

It was here at Caraguaytay that don Venancio died of exhaustion and General Barrios, the ex-Minister of War was excecuted before his wife and his sister-in-law. Inocencia and Rafaela were thrashed daily but not cruelly enough to kill them.

Deeper into the regions unknown the caravans proceeded and the executions went on. The heroic struggle continued all through the year 1869. In the outside world Lopez was looked upon as a fantastic patriot who was sacrificing his country for an ideal. Was he a patriot or fanatic? The two were now the same. His countrymen both feared and loved him. If they lost an eye he told them how to go on fighting with the good one. If they lost a leg he told them to stand on what was left. Very often in the heat of battle his soldiers would crawl back to die at his feet like dogs.

Eliza was living in a strange world of massacres, mosquitos and malaria—nightmares from which there was no escape except through fantasy or death. She allowed events to take their course, events which she could no longer control.

General MacMahon seemed to be their only hope. Would America come to their aid? That seemed to be a burning question. Every day she prayed for news of him. The idea that they would eventually be rescued by the United States gave them strength to go on fighting.

In January, 1870, Lopez crossed La Cordillera de Amambay and entered what was known as La Picada de Chiriguelo. Guards with fixed bayonets stood over prisoners, compelling them to cut a path through the virgin forests of Ilex Paraguensis to force a passage for Madame Lynch's carriage that preceded the wagons, bullock carts and the entire drifting cavalcade.

Prisoners, priests, camp followers, soldiers, old men and young, hollow eyed and feverish, huddled around a carriage in which sat an indomitable Irishwoman with an enigmatic face. To this plight Lopez had brought the nation. These emaciated people, the nomads, these living corpses were all that remained of Paraguay.

On the 14th of February, 1870, the straggling remnants of an army emerged at Cerro Cora, a natural amphitheatre, pursued by an enemy of ten times its strength. Situated in the extreme north-east corner of Paraguay, close to the Bolivian border, Cerro Cora is approached by two gorges, one known as Chiriguelo and the other as La Picada de Yateho.

The Paraguayans pitched camp in this vast semi-circular arena with the trees rising in tiers, crowned with bright garlands of parasitical lianas: flowers that are there own funeral wreaths, winding themselves in knots and strangling the trees that fight for their very existence. At eventide countless insects, mosquitos, wild bees and humming birds engaged in their quickening activity. Jaguars sharpened their claws, smelling the decaying flesh of their intended victim. The women buried their dead at night, carrying the lifeless bodies, as brittle as match sticks, shoulder high. Red monkeys perched on the twisted branches of trees, making the forest tremble with their incessant jabberings, and sloths vegetated, flattening against the trees and adding their melancholy "Ai, Ai, Ai," to the sounds of the night.

On the 24th of February Lopez awoke, resolved to have a medal engraved in commemoration of the campaign of Amambay. He seemed to know that it would be his last battle and went to much trouble in choosing a design worthy of the historical occasion. He pondered a long time over the colour of the ribbon. Should it be the blue of Eliza's eyes or the colour of the skies of Paraguay. Only one person was to be exempt from receiving this honour and that was his mother, the woman who had bestowed on him the gift of life; a compliment that he returned by signing her death warrant. She must die. A deed that was ordered to be carried out on the following day. For months his shrouded mind had been brooding over her infamy. To have been disgraced before his people. To have been accused of being a bastard was a degradation beyond belief. It was true that she had recanted but the dishonour remained. The shame could only be wiped out by death. She must die branded in history with the stigma of having been put to death by her own son, the Marshal-President, who despite her iniquity still loved her. Surely, only death could wipe away her sins.

Dona Juana was beyond human care or suffering. The threads of her emotions had snapped. Resigned, she spent the night in prayer for the redemption of her first born's immortal soul.

In the darkest hour before the dawn on the day assigned for his mother's death the unconquered Marshal's pitiable outposts were surprised by the Brazilian cavalry. The wavering bugles sounded the alarm and echoed thinly and discordantly in the valleys. Lopez called for his horse, and with some difficulty because of his weight, was helped to mount by his orderly. In the confusion there was barely time to say good-bye to Eliza or to his children. He dug his silver spurs into his horse and endeavoured to escape. Madame Lynch gathered her sons about her and climbed into the cumbersome vehicle that stood by in readiness.

The carriage could barely proceed, weighed down as it was with boxes of clothes, silver and provisions. A queen in all but name, now fleeing from her Kingdom, Eliza hoped to elude her enemies in the jungle.

Lopez cantered towards the valley and was about to cross the river when the animal stumbled on some loose stones and he was overthrown into the swamp. The Marshal regained his balance and stood up to his knees in water, but was immediately surrounded by Brazilian soldiers. Trapped and maddened he tried to cut a path through their midst with his sabre but at that moment a corporal by the name of Lacerda, known as Chico Diablo, acting contrary to the strictest orders threw a spear that wounded the President in the stomach.

Lopez fell. He struggled on to his knees and with superhuman effort managed to wade across the stream. A Brazilian General who rode up at that moment, summoned him to surrender. Lopez's only answer was a revolver shot. But Chico Diablo had dealt a mortal blow and the unconquered Marshal drew himself up to his full height and exclaimed, "Muero con mi patria" "I perish with my country," and fell dead in the swamp. His body was immediately besieged by flies.

With his death, that hypnotic spell that Lopez had always excercised over his people seemed to break. For one second they floundered like a rudderless ship and then their suppressed hatred burst forth like a released dam with a menacing roar. The camp followers, even those who were about to expire through weakness and exposure, found breath to delay their dying gasps and ran towards Madame Lynch, resolved that she should die.

Howls, jeers and taunts, threatening and uncontrollable, rent the air. Eliza sat in her carriage which had stuck in the stream. Disdainfully, she stared at these scarecrows, these emaciated corpses, inhabitants of a world where, it seemed, only she and her sons had retained the vestiges of human beings.

At this moment the Brazilian rode up and overtook her carriage, "Lopez is dead", they shouted regardless of her feelings. Pancho, the eldest son, fired from the carriage window and wounded a Brazilian Sergeant. A lance thrust pierced his heart and he fell dead across his mother's knee.

By now the howling mob of bald, gnarled, naked women were clamouring round the carriage intent on tearing her to pieces; "Death. Death to Lavinche."

The same women that Eliza had raised to an army now bayed for her death.

It was only the Brazilian cavalry, bearing down on the unruly mob with their sabres, that saved Eliza's life. The sisters of Lopez stood by and cursed her. Not unnaturally they looked on her with loathing and blamed her for their misfortunes. They swore it was her avarice, her lust for power and her ambitions that had brought them to this plight. When dona Juana was told that her son was dead, she burst into tears. "God have mercy on his soul." She, who had been sentenced to death and had only been saved by his timely end now prayed for his salvation. "No Mother, Do not weep," said her daughters. "This man was not a brother, nor a son— he was a monster."

"Death. Death to Lavinche."

She was still in her carriage surrounded by her three surviving sons and holding in her arms her dead firstborn when the Comte d'Eu rode up to offer his condolences. With great dignity the Irish woman alighted from her conveyance and surrendered Paraguay.

Protected by the enemy, from the claws of her adopted country-women, she was escorted to the place where her consort had fallen. He was partly submerged in the water. Flies had settled around his eyes.

While the Brazilian soldiers out of respect for her feelings, withdrew some distance away, Madame Lynch together with her sons scraped out a shallow grave with their bare hands. In this makeshift burial ground they placed the Marshal and his eldest son. No word was spoken, no prayer, nor funeral oration was said. No muffled drums or fanfare was sounded. They trod the earth back into place and put some stones to protect the bodies from the scavengers of the jungle.

Only Madame Lynch mourned the man, who, had the battle gone the other way, would have made her Queen of the River Plate.

Once she had finished her task, she went up to the Comte d'Eu and said "Sir, I am ready."

The story should end here but not even tragedy concludes smoothly.

CHAPTER THIRTY-EIGHT

EPILOGUE

Madame Lynch received nothing but kindness and consideration from the Brazilians who sent her back to Europe with all the honours that a chivalrous conqueror could bestow on a gallant woman who was at the same time a brave and vanquished foe. On her arrival in London she took a house in Thurloe Place. In spite of a lifetime of adventure she was only thirty six. Cunningham-Graham who had occasion to observe her writes; "I saw her several times in London in 1873 or 1874, getting into her carriage at a house she had in Thurloe Square or Hyde Park Gate. She was then apparently about forty years of age. Of middle height, well made, beginning to put on a little flesh, with her abundant fair hair just flecked with grey. In her well made Parisian clothes, she looked more French than English, and had no touch of that untidiness that so often marks the Irishwoman. She was still handsome and distinguished looking. Her face was oval and her lips a little full, her eyes were large and grey if I remember rightly, and her appearance did not seem that of one who had looked death so often in the face, lived for so long in circumstances so strange and terrifying, buried her lover and her son with her own hands, and lived to tell the tale."

Anyone seeing her around this time at the Brompton Oratory on a Sunday morning, tall and stately, accompanied by her three sons would not have credited her story.

Vanquished on the battlefield she now took up arms in a legal struggle and made the journey to Edinburgh to bring a lawsuit against Doctor Stewart.

As far back as 1866 she had requested Doctor Stewart to send £4,000 out of the country on her behalf. The demand was followed by a similar one from Lopez in 1868 when he had asked Doctor Stewart to remit £11,000 to the Royal Bank of Scotland. Lopez had named a certain M. Jelot of Paris to act as his representative in Europe. When the Frenchman had gone to claim the money, however, he found that Doctor Stewart had stopped payment. Subsequently Doctor Stewart, who had been taken prisoner by the Brazilians, asserted that Lopez had robbed him of personal property amounting to £20,000 as a consequence of which the £15,000 lying to his account in Edinburgh was rightfully his.

The case Stewart versus Jelot was tried at Edinburgh before the Lord Chief Justice.

As the Times reported on August 3rd, 1871—

"In the second division of the Court of Session, Edinburgh on Saturday, Judgement was given in a bill of exceptions and application in the new trial in the action raised by Doctor William Stewart for the reduction of a bill of Exchange for £4,000. Dr. Stewart granted the bill to Madame Lynch while in Paraguay but he alleged that it had been taken from him under force and fear".

After much deliberation a special jury decided that Doctor Stewart had acted under pressure and the case was left pending until M. Jelot or Madame Lynch could produce fresh evidence to the contrary and, as this proved impossible, they were obliged to drop the case.

Fifteen thousand pounds the poorer, Eliza returned to Paris and settled in a house in the Rue de Rivoli which she bought with the money that General MacMahon had managed to bring out of Paraguay.

On the General's return to Washington, there had been a great political controversy about the two American Ministers accredited to Asuncion. Whereas General MacMahon had upheld the altruistic motives of Marshal Lopez and was a staunch supporter of Madame Lynch, Washburn had done his utmost to blacken their characters. All he had succeeded in doing was irreparable harm to himself. Although it was never proved that he had participated in the conspiracy, he was dismissed from Diplomatic Service for not having upheld better the dignity of the United States of America.

For five years Eliza lived in a grand scale in Paris and entertained lavishly but her assets could not be made to last forever and in 1875 she decided to return to Asuncion to claim her inheritance. She travelled in the Royal Mail packet boat "City of Limerick" as far as Buenos Aires where she found she was not forgotten and was taken to see a play based on the story of her life, entitled "Madame Lynch".

From Buenos Aires she took the river steamer up the Paraguay. She gazed with deep emotion on the dismantled forts of Curupaity, Riachuelo and Humaita. To her intense humiliation and especially after her favourable reception in Buenos Aires she found that the new Head of State, Senor Jovellanos, a relative of her erstwhile Lady in Waiting, had declared her a persona non grata and she was refused permission to land in Asuncion. Napoleon standing on the decks of the Bellephoron could not have felt more bitter than Eliza Lynch barred from setting foot in Paraguay.

She ceded the title deeds of her lands, three thousand and five leagues, according to the Marshal's will to her sons Enrique and Carlos who remained in Buenos Aires to establish their claims. As she embraced them she said "My life may have been one of sin but yours is blameless. Remember you are the sons of a man whose fame shall grow with each passing year."

She returned to Europe with her youngest son Leopoldo who died on the journey. She had no more tears to shed.

Restless of spirit, she set out on a pilgrimage for the Holy Land and lived in Jerusalem for three years; but Paris always drew her back. Once more she was in dire straits and forced to seek a livelihood. By one of those strange turns of fortune she found employment in a house of ill repute, but whereas formerly she had reigned supreme, now she was merely the

Madame. The complete cycle had come round. She presided at the gaming table like a ghost of her former self, aware now that in the ultimate throw all men are losers. Regrets, she had no regrets, only resentment because of the knocks that God had given her. She was never to know acceptance, resignation or tranquility. She was hard because life had made her hard and man has no weapons against fate. To the end she could only repeat to herself the age old Spanish saying "Hombre propone y Dios dispone" or in other words "Man proposes and God disposes."

On the 25th July, 1886, she died in poverty, according to Cunningham-Graham, and the Municipality of Paris paid for her burial which took place at Père Lachaise.

And still the gods would not allow her to rest in peace. Half a century later, at the request of the Government of Paraguay, the mortal remains of Eliza Eloisa Lynch were taken back to Asuncion, the capital of her adopted country. Eliza, who the last time had been turned away, was received with every conceivable honour. Even Marshal Lopez would have been gratified by the magnificence of the tribute paid to his consort. Guards of honour, salvos, massed bands and speeches preceded her to the tomb, the *Pantéon de los Heroes,* a memorial to Eliza Lynch who, for good or evil, had been all but Queen of Paraguay.

BIBLIOGRAPHY

Spiritual Conquest of Paraguay—Father Ruiz Montoya

Portrait of a Dictator—R. B. Cunningham-Graham. (Putnam, 1933)

History of Paraguay—Washburn, American Minister in Asuncion

The Man in Paraguay—Colonel Thompson

El Mariscal Solano Lopez—Juan E. O'Leary

Histiria del Paraguay—Blasgaray

The Battlefields of Paraguay—Burton

La Tirania en el Paraguay—Cecilio Baez

Seven Eventful Years in Paraguay—Masterman

El Mariscal Francesco Solano Lopez—Cecilio Baez. (Asuncion, 1926)

Women on Horseback—William Barrett. (Peter Davies, 1938)

Land of Women—Katharina von Dombrowski. (Little Brown & Co., Boston) Translated from the German.

Cieu Vidas Paraguayas—Carlos Zubizarreta. (Ediciones Nizza, 1961)

Solano Lopez—Arturo Bray (Buenos Aires, 1943)

Hombres y Epocas del Paraguay—Arturo Bray (Buenos Aires, 1943)

El Supremo—Edward Lucas White (Mitchells English Bookstore, Buenos Aires)

Padre Pedro Francesco Xavier de Charlevoix (Madrid 1910)

Letters of Paraguay—J. P. and W. P. Robertson. (John Murray)

Resumen de la Histiria del Paraguay desde la Epoca de la Conquesta Hasta el ano 1880—Cecilio Baez. (Asuncion 1910)

In Jesuit Land—W. H. Koebel. (Stanley Paul)

Histiria de la Companio de Jesus en la Provincia del Paraguay, Extracts from the Archives of the Indes. P.O. Pablo Pastells, S. J.